Illuminate
Publishing

WJEC
A2 Biology

Study and
Revision Guide

Gareth Rowlands

D0487180

Published in 2011 by Illuminate Publishing Ltd, P.O Box 1160,
Cheltenham, Gloucestershire GL50 9RW

Orders: Please visit www.illuminatepublishing.com
or email sales@illuminatepublishing.com

© Gareth Rowlands

The moral rights of the author have been asserted.

All rights reserved. No part of this book may be reprinted, reproduced or utilised in any
form or by any electronic, mechanical, or other means, now known or hereafter invented,
including photocopying and recording, or in any information storage and retrieval
system, without permission in writing from the publishers.

British Library Cataloguing in Publication Data

A catalogue record for this book is available from the British Library

ISBN 978-0-9568401-5-8

Printed by T J International, Padstow, Cornwall

The publisher's policy is to use papers that are natural, renewable and recyclable
products made from wood grown in sustainable forests. The logging and manufacturing
processes are expected to conform to the environmental regulations of the country of
origin.

Every effort has been made to contact copyright holders of material reproduced in this
book. If notified, the publishers will be pleased to rectify any errors or omissions at the
earliest opportunity.

This material has been endorsed by WJEC and offers high quality support for the
delivery of WJEC qualifications. While this material has been through a WJEC quality
assurance process, all responsibility for the content remains with the publisher.

Editor: Geoff Tuttle

Design and layout: Nigel Harriss

Acknowledgements

I am very grateful to the team at Illuminate Publishing for their professionalism, support
and guidance throughout this project. It has been a pleasure to work so closely with
them.

The author and publisher wish to thank:

Dr John Ford for his thorough review of the book and expert insights and observations.

We are indebted to Mike Ebbsworth of WJEC whose unstinting help and
encouragement from the beginning made this whole undertaking possible.

Dr Janet Jones of WJEC.

Contents

How to use this book

As a Principal Examiner for the WJEC specification I have written this study guide to help you be aware of what is required, and structured the content to guide you through to success in the WJEC Biology A2 examination.

Knowledge and Understanding

The **first section** of the book covers the key knowledge required for the examination.

There are notes for the compulsory sections of each examination:

BY4 – Metabolism, Microbiology and Homeostasis

BY5 – Environment, Genetics and Evolution.

In addition, I have tried to give you additional pointers so that you can develop your work:

- Any of the terms in the WJEC specification can be used as the basis of a question, so I have highlighted those terms and offered definitions.

- There are 'Quickfire' questions designed to test your knowledge and understanding of the material.

- I have offered examination advice based on experience of what candidates need to do to attain the highest grades.

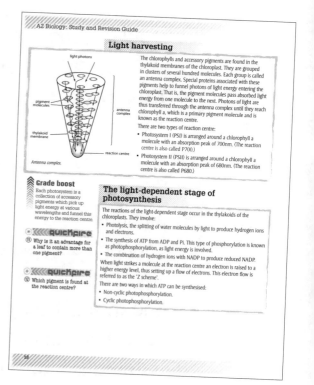

Exam Practice and Technique

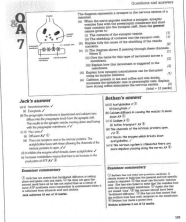

The **second section** of the book covers the key skills for examination success and offers you examples based on real-life responses to examination questions. First you will be guided into an understanding of how the examination system works, and then offered clues to success.

A variety of structured and essay questions are provided in this section. Each essay includes the marking points expected followed by actual samples of candidates' responses. A variety of structured questions are also provided, together with typical responses and comments. They offer a guide as to the standard that is required, and the commentary will explain why the responses gained the marks that they did.

Most importantly, I advise that you should take responsibility for your own learning and not rely on your teachers to give you notes or tell you how to gain the grades that you require. You should look for additional notes to support your study into WJEC Biology.

I advise that you look at the WJEC website www.wjec.co.uk. In particular, you need to be aware of the specification. Look for specimen examination papers and mark schemes. You may find past papers useful as well.

Good luck with your revision.

Gareth Rowlands

Knowledge and Understanding

BY4 Metabolism, Microbiology and Homeostasis

Green plants carry out the process of photosynthesis to capture sunlight energy in chemical form. The resulting energy-containing molecules are used to store energy but, if broken down directly, the energy would be released in an uncontrollable way. Instead energy is transferred, from molecules such as glucose, to an intermediate energy source, ATP, which is released in small, manageable quantities. ATP is a reservoir of potential chemical energy and acts as a common intermediate in metabolism, linking energy-requiring and energy-yielding reactions.

Advances in biotechnology have allowed humans to manipulate micro-organisms on an industrial scale in vessels called fermenters. This has enabled products such as hormones and antibiotics to be mass produced. Population growth is affected by environmental resistance factors. Competition exists between individuals of the same species and between individuals of different species. Micro-organisms play a key role in the cycling of nutrients.

In order to survive, plants and animals must react to changes in their external environment. They possess mechanisms for detecting such changes and bringing about appropriate responses in order to maintain a constant internal environment. The kidneys play an important role in osmoregulation as well as excreting the nitrogenous waste products of metabolism.

Since the structures that detect changes may be some distance from those that respond, a means of communication within the body is required. Animals have nervous systems and hormonal mechanisms, whereas plant responses are regulated by hormones alone.

Revision checklist

Tick column 1 when you have completed brief revision notes.
Tick column 2 when you think you have a good grasp of the topic.
Tick column 3 during final revision when you feel you have mastery of the topic.

		1	2	3	Notes
p8	**Energy and ATP**	✓			
p8	The structure of ATP	✓			
p8	The importance of ATP	✓			
p9	The uses and advantages of ATP as a source of energy	✓			
p9	The roles of ATP	✓			
p10	**Respiration**	✓			
p11	Glycolysis	✓			
p11	The link reaction	✓			
p11	Krebs cycle	✓			
p12	The electron transport chain	✓			

Key term

Activation energy = the energy needed to start a chemical reaction. You may recall from unit BY1 that enzymes lower the activation energy to make a reaction begin.

» Pointer

ATP is often called the 'universal energy currency in living organisms' as it provides a common source of energy for many different chemical reactions. ATP is therefore a short-term energy store of the cell.

Grade boost

The conversion of ATP to ADP is a reversible reaction. ATP is synthesised during reactions that release energy and it is hydrolysed to provide energy for those reactions that need it.

Grade boost

Because of the instability of its phosphate bonds ATP is a good immediate energy donor. However, fats and carbohydrates are far better long-term energy stores.

Energy and ATP

Respiration involves the gradual release of energy in a number of small steps rather than the rapid release of energy all at once. Glucose is broken down by means of enzymes through a number of intermediate compounds, with the controlled release of small quantities of energy at each stage. These reactions provide the energy to produce a molecule called adenosine triphosphate or ATP.

The structure of ATP

ATP is a nucleotide consisting of an organic base, adenine, a five-carbon sugar, ribose, and a sequence of three phosphate groups linked together.

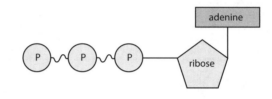

The structure of ATP.

The importance of ATP

The uncontrolled release of energy from glucose would result in an increase in temperature that would destroy cells. Instead living organisms use the gradual release of energy in small steps to produce ATP. ADP is converted to ATP by the addition of phosphate molecules. Since energy is used up in the production of ATP, it is referred to as an endergonic reaction. The amount of energy needed to add each phosphate molecule is 30 kJ mol^{-1}. The phosphate groups are held in place by high-energy bonds.

ATP can be hydrolysed to release energy as required. When ATP is broken down to ADP and phosphate this is referred to as an exergonic reaction since energy is released. The hydrolysis of ATP to ADP is catalysed by the enzyme ATPase and the removal of the terminal phosphate yields 30 kJ mol^{-1} of free energy.

$$\text{ATP} \longrightarrow \text{ADP} + \text{Pi} + 30\,\text{kJ mol}^{-1}$$

When a phosphate molecule is transferred from ATP to another molecule it makes it more reactive and so lowers the **activation energy** of that molecule.

The addition of phosphate to ADP is called **phosphorylation**. ATP is therefore a means of transferring free energy from energy-rich compounds, like glucose, to cellular reactions where energy is needed.

There are three forms of phosphorylation:

- Oxidative phosphorylation, which occurs on the membranes of the mitochondria during aerobic respiration and involves the process of electron transport.
- Photophosphorylation, which occurs on the membranes of the chloroplasts during photosynthesis.
- Substrate-level phosphorylation, which occurs when phosphate groups are transferred from donor molecules to ADP to make ATP.

The uses and advantages of ATP as a source of energy

There are several advantages in having ATP as an intermediate source of energy compared with glucose. These include:

- Only one enzyme is needed to release energy from ATP, while many are needed in the case of glucose.
- ATP releases energy in small amounts when and where needed, whereas glucose contains large amounts of energy that may not be needed immediately.
- ATP provides a common source of energy for many different chemical reactions, increasing efficiency and control by the cell. ATP is in fact known as the 'universal energy currency in living organisms'.

The roles of ATP

ATP provides the necessary energy for:

- Metabolic processes – to build large, complex molecules from smaller, simpler molecules. For example, the synthesis of DNA from nucleotides and polypeptides from amino acids.
- Active transport – to change the shape of carrier proteins in plasma membranes to allow molecules or ions to be moved against a concentration gradient.
- Movement – for muscle contraction.
- Nerve transmission – sodium-potassium pumps actively transport sodium and potassium ions across the axon plasma membrane.
- Synthesis of materials within cells.
- Secretion – the packaging and transport of secretory products into vesicles in cells.

Key term

Phosphorylation = the addition of phosphate to ADP.

 quickfire

① Name a cell type which contains a large number of mitochondria.

≫ *Pointer*

ATP is not stored; it has to be synthesised as required. The rate of production keeps pace with demand. A metabolically active cell may require 2 million ATP molecules per second! Cells do not store large quantities of ATP but maintain a supply which lasts only a few seconds.

 quickfire

② Why is ATP sometimes referred to as 'an immediate energy source'?

Respiration

Grade boost

During glycolysis the breakdown of one molecule of glucose produces two molecules of pyruvate, two molecules of ATP and two molecules of reduced NAD.

≫ Pointer

You are not required to know the names of all the intermediates, only those given in the diagram.

Grade boost

FAD replaces NAD as the first acceptor at point X in the Krebs cycle.

≫ Pointer

The names of the intermediates of glycolysis and Krebs cycle are not required.

Grade boost

Examination questions often ask you to indicate the points where carbon dioxide and hydrogen are released.

Aerobic respiration can be divided into four distinct but linked stages:

- Glycolysis
- The link reaction
- Krebs cycle
- The electron transport chain.

The stages are summarised in the diagram.

Summary of respiration.

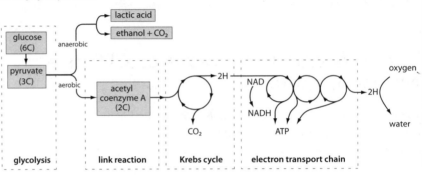

Summary of glycolysis, link reaction and Krebs cycle

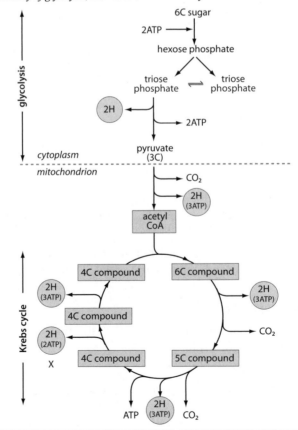

Glycolysis

Glycolysis takes place in the cytoplasm.

- The glucose molecule is first activated by phosphorylation to make it more reactive by the addition of two molecules of ATP to form hexose phosphate.

- The 6-carbon hexose phosphate is split into two molecules of triose phosphate (3-carbon sugar).

- Triose phosphate is converted to pyruvic acid. This involves the removal of hydrogen and its transfer to a hydrogen carrier molecule called NAD to form reduced NAD. Two of the steps transfer sufficient energy for the synthesis of ATP. This yields a total of four ATP molecules. The ATP is formed by substrate level phosphorylation.

The link reaction

The energy which remains in the pyruvate molecules produced during glycolysis can only be released aerobically in the Krebs cycle. The link reaction links glycolysis to the Krebs cycle:

- Pyruvic acid diffuses from the cytoplasm to the mitochondrial matrix.
- The pyruvate is **decarboxylated**.
- The pyruvate is also **dehydrogenated** and the hydrogen released is accepted by NAD to form reduced NAD.
- The 2-carbon acetate formed then combines with coenzyme A to form acetyl coenzyme A, which then enters the Krebs cycle.

Krebs cycle

The function of the Krebs cycle is a means of liberating energy from carbon bonds to provide ATP and reduced NAD (and FAD), with the release of carbon dioxide. Reduced NAD (and FAD) deliver the hydrogen to the electron transport system in the inner mitochondrial membrane so acting as triggers for this system.

- Acetyl CoA enters the Krebs cycle by combining with a 4-carbon acid, to form a 6-carbon compound, the CoA is regenerated.

- The 6-carbon compound undergoes reactions during which carbon dioxide and hydrogen atoms are removed. After the acetate fragment is broken down, the remaining 4-carbon residue undergoes conversion to regenerate the 4-carbon compound which combines with more acetyl CoA.

- Two of the steps involve **decarboxylation**, and four of the steps involve **dehydrogenation**.

- The hydrogen atoms produced are collected by two different carriers with the formation of three molecules of NADH/H$^+$ (reduced NAD) and one molecule of FADH$_2$ (reduced FAD).

Key terms

Decarboxylation = the removal of carbon dioxide.

Dehydrogenation = the removal of hydrogen.

≫ Pointer

Although four molecules of ATP are produced in glycolysis, two are required for the initial phosphorylation of glucose. So the net production is two molecules.

Grade boost

If aerobic conditions occur, the two molecules of reduced NAD produced during glycolysis have the potential to produce an additional six molecules of ATP.

≫ Pointer

You are not required to know the names of all the enzymes involved at each stage but you should know that dehydrogenase enzymes catalyse the removal of hydrogen atoms, and decarboxylases catalyse the removal of carbon dioxide.

Grade boost

Don't forget that for each molecule of glucose two molecules of acetyl coenzyme A enter the Krebs cycle. So the cycle turns twice for each glucose molecule.

Grade boost

There is only one occasion in the cycle where FAD acts as a carrier. If NAD is the first carrier then there are three pumps involved in the electron transport system. As there is no pump associated with FAD, only two pumps are involved and two ATPs are produced in this system.

Grade boost

Oxidative phosphorylation takes place on the membranes of the mitochondrion. The arrangement of membranes provides a large surface area for the chemical reactions of respiration to take place. The cristae are lined with stalked particles which contain the ATP synthetase enzymes.

- Thus, for each turn of the cycle, the overall production is one ATP, three reduced NAD and one reduced FAD. Since these are produced from the breakdown of one molecule of pyruvate, the two molecules produced in glycolysis will give double this yield.

The electron transport chain

The electron transport chain is a series of carriers and pumps, releasing energy in the form of ATP.

The carbon dioxide is a waste product of respiration but the hydrogen atoms (or more particularly the electrons they possess) are a potential source of energy. Hydrogen atoms are carried by the coenzymes NAD and FAD into the electron transport chain.

If NADH is the initial acceptor, for each pair of hydrogen atoms involved enough energy is released for the synthesis of three molecules of ATP. Where $FADH_2$ appears in the Krebs cycle, only two molecules of ATP are produced.

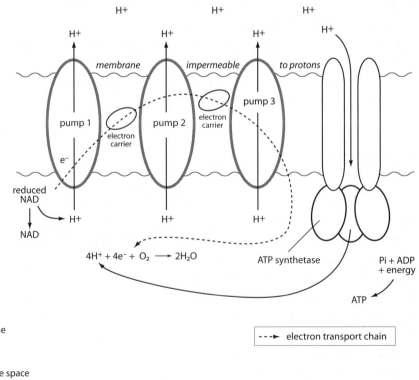

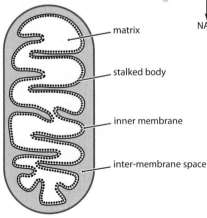

Mitochondrion with detail of electron transport chain.

The following is referred to as the **chemiosmotic theory**, which summarises the synthesis of ATP using the electron transport chain.

- The hydrogen atoms combine with NAD.
- The reduced NAD donate the electrons of the hydrogen atoms they are carrying to the first pump.
- The carrier thus becomes reoxidised and releases protons into the matrix. The charged pump then pumps protons into the space between the inner and outer membranes.
- Electrons with a slightly reduced energy level are transferred by a carrier to the next pump.
- A high concentration of protons builds up in the inter-membrane space because the inner membrane is impermeable to protons except at certain sites.
- One of these sites is the enzyme ATP synthetase.
- The protons are able to flow back into the matrix via channels formed by ATP synthetase molecules in the stalked bodies.
- This flow acts as a driving force to combine ADP and inorganic phosphate to synthesise ATP.
- The electrons from the last pump are taken up by oxygen, which combines with protons to form water. This reaction is catalysed by the enzyme oxidase. Oxygen is therefore the final electron acceptor. If oxygen was not present then there would be a build-up of protons in the matrix and no gradient across the membrane.

Key term

Chemiosmotic theory = a model to explain the synthesis of ATP. The theory proposes that the energy for ATP synthesis originates from the electrochemical gradient of protons across a membrane.

≫ Pointer

The names of the proton pumps and electron carriers in the electron transport system are not required.

quickfire

③ State precisely where in the cell the following processes occur:
(a) glycolysis
(b) Krebs cycle.

quickfire

④ Explain the role of oxygen in the electron transport chain.

quickfire

⑤ Explain the advantage of the surface of the inner mitochondrial membrane being highly folded to form cristae.

≫ *Pointer*

Don't forget that two molecules of acetyl coenzyme A enter the Krebs cycle for each molecule of glucose.

◉≪≪ quickfire

⑥ Calculate the efficiency of anaerobic respiration, if each ATP molecule yields approximately 30KJ of energy and the complete oxidation of a molecule of glucose yields 2880KJ.

≫ *Pointer*

Anaerobic respiration, leading to the production of ethanol, occurs in some micro-organisms and some cells of higher plants, e.g. root cells under waterlogged conditions. Lactic acid production occurs most commonly in muscle tissue as a result of strenuous exercise.

Energy budget

The number of ATP molecules produced from the breakdown of one molecule of glucose. Remember:

- Some ATP molecules are produced directly by substrate level phosphorylation.
- Most ATP is produced by oxidative phosphorylation.
- Each NADH can produce 3 ATP molecules.
- Each FADH can produce 2 ATP molecules.

Glycolysis

4 ATPs made directly by substrate level phosphorylation but 2 ATPs used.

Total = 2 ATP

Two NADH (a potential for an additional 6 molecules of ATP)

Link reaction

Two NADH (2 x 3 = 6)

Total = 6 ATP

Krebs cycle

Six NADH (3 x 6 = 18)

Two FADH (2 x 2 = 4)

2 ATPs made directly by substrate level phosphorylation

Total = 24 ATP

This gives a total of 38 molecules of ATP from each molecule of glucose.

Anaerobic respiration

In the absence of oxygen:

- Only the first stage of respiration, glycolysis, can take place.
- The reduced NAD (and FAD) cannot be reoxidised and therefore made available to pick up more hydrogen, and so the link reaction and the Krebs cycle cannot take place.
- The yield of ATP is two molecules of ATP.

Fermentation

This takes place in yeast when the pyruvate is converted to alcohol and carbon dioxide.

- The pyruvate is first decarboxylated to produce ethanal.
- The hydrogen released during glycolysis is passed on to NAD.
- The reduced NAD then passes the hydrogen to ethanal which is reduced to ethanol.

Lactic acid formation in muscle

During vigorous exercise the human body cannot get sufficient oxygen to the muscle cells. Instead of respiring aerobically, the cells can only produce ATP by glycolysis.

The reduced NAD produced during glycolysis passes its hydrogen directly to pyruvate, thus reducing it to lactate.

Alternative respiratory substrates

In addition to glucose, under certain circumstances, fats and proteins can be used as respiratory substrates.

Lipids

- Fat provides an energy store and is used as a respiratory substrate when carbohydrate levels are low. It has to be split into its constituent molecules of glycerol and fatty acids, first by hydrolysis and then the glycerol is converted into a 3-carbon sugar which enters the Krebs cycle via triose phosphate yielding ATP molecules.

- The long fatty acid chain molecules are split into 2-carbon fragments which enter the pathway as acetyl CoA. Very large numbers of ATP molecules are built up during the process, the precise number depending on the length of the hydrocarbon chain of the fatty acid. This is because the hydrogen ions released are picked up by NAD and fed into the electron transport chains.

- For this reason, one gram of fat releases more than twice as much energy as one gram of carbohydrate.

Protein

Protein can be used as a respiratory substrate but only when an individual is suffering from starvation.

In prolonged starvation the tissue protein is mobilised to supply energy, and whenever dietary energy supplies are inadequate, the protein component of the food is diverted for energy purposes. The protein is hydrolysed into its constituent amino acids and then it is deaminated in the liver. The amino group is converted into urea and excreted and the residue is converted to either acetyl CoA, pyruvic acid or some other Krebs cycle intermediate, and oxidised. Protein is very rarely used as a respiratory substrate, usually only when all reserves of carbohydrate and fat have been depleted.

Grade boost

Build-up of lactic acid in muscle causes cramp. When oxygen becomes available again the lactic acid is broken down in the liver. Most is converted to glycogen and stored for further energy release.

quickfire

(7) Which releases most energy, a gram of fat or a gram of carbohydrate?

Grade boost

Most metabolic pathways lead to acetyl CoA, which is a kind of crossroads in metabolism. As well as its formation during the oxidation of carbohydrates, it is formed during the oxidation of fats and proteins and represents a common pathway by which the products of all three are fed into the Krebs cycle.

Photosynthesis

Summary of photosynthesis

Photosynthesis takes place in the chloroplasts. These are found in the mesophyll cells and guard cells of green leaves. In the chloroplasts the energy of sunlight is trapped by the pigment chlorophyll.

Photosynthesis takes place in two stages: the light-dependent and the light-independent reaction.

The site of photosynthesis was detected in 1887 by a botanist called Englemann.

Englemann devised an experiment to determine which wavelengths of light were the most effective in carrying out photosynthesis using a filamentous green alga, each cell of which contains a ribbon-like chloroplast shaped in the form of a spiral. He placed the algae in a suspension of motile, aerobic bacteria which were evenly distributed, and exposed the algal cells to a range of wavelengths. After a short period of time he noticed that the bacteria clustered near to the chloroplasts at the blue and red wavelengths. This was because these wavelengths resulted in increased photosynthesis, which produced more oxygen and so attracted more of the bacteria.

Summary of photosynthesis.

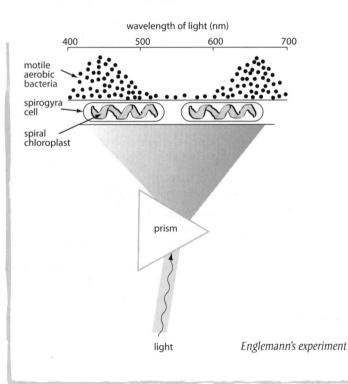

Englemann's experiment

8 Which two products of the light-dependent stage are used in the light-independent stage?

9 Why did the bacteria in the experiment cluster at certain areas of the alga?

Photosynthetic pigments

In photosynthesis different wavelengths of light are trapped by different pigments. In flowering plants there are two main types of pigments: chlorophylls and carotenoids. Chlorophylls absorb light energy mainly in the red and blue-violet regions of the spectrum, whereas the carotenoids absorb the light energy from the blue-violet region of the spectrum. The two main types of carotenoids, the carotenes and the xanthophylls, act as accessory pigments.

Absorption and action spectra

Experimentally, the different pigments can be shown to absorb different wavelengths by making separate solutions of each pigment and shining light through them. This absorption spectrum can be represented as a graph that indicates how much light a particular pigment absorbs at each wavelength. For example, chlorophyll absorbs wavelengths in the blue and red parts of the spectrum. However, this does not indicate whether the wavelengths are actually used in photosynthesis.

The action spectrum is a graph that shows the rate of photosynthesis at different wavelengths of light. That is, the amount of carbohydrate synthesised by plants exposed to different wavelengths of light. If one graph is superimposed on the other, it can be seen that there is a close correlation between the absorption spectrum and the action spectrum. This suggests that the pigments are responsible for absorbing the light used in photosynthesis.

Graph showing the relationship between the absorption spectrum and the action spectrum.

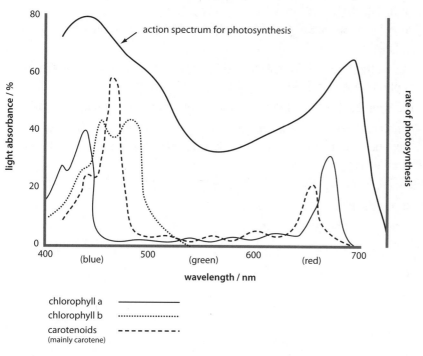

chlorophyll a ———
chlorophyll b ··············
carotenoids ------
(mainly carotene)

>> *Pointer*

The role of photosynthetic pigments is to absorb light energy and to convert it to chemical energy.

Grade boost

Chlorophyll absorbs only certain wavelengths of light and reflects others. This explains why green plants appear green!

(10) What is the difference between an absorption spectrum and action spectrum?

Grade boost

It is incorrect to state that 'pigments absorb light'. They absorb light energy. (Light energy may also be expressed in terms of 'quanta' and 'photons'.)

Light harvesting

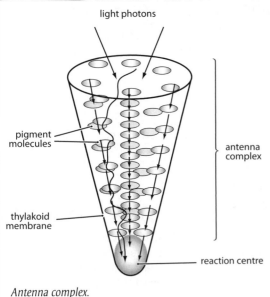

light photons

pigment molecules

thylakoid membrane

antenna complex

reaction centre

Antenna complex.

The chlorophylls and accessory pigments are found in the thylakoid membranes of the chloroplast. They are grouped in clusters of several hundred molecules. Each group is called an antenna complex. Special proteins associated with these pigments help to funnel photons of light energy entering the chloroplast. That is, the pigment molecules pass absorbed light energy from one molecule to the next. Photons of light are thus transferred through the antenna complex until they reach chlorophyll a, which is a primary pigment molecule and is known as the reaction centre.

There are two types of reaction centre:

- Photosystem I (PSI) is arranged around a chlorophyll a molecule with an absorption peak of 700nm. (The reaction centre is also called P700.)
- Photosystem II (PSII) is arranged around a chlorophyll a molecule with an absorption peak of 680nm. (The reaction centre is also called P680.)

Grade boost

Each photosystem is a collection of accessory pigments which pick up light energy at various wavelengths and funnel this energy to the reaction centre.

quickpire

⑪ Why is it an advantage for a leaf to contain more than one pigment?

quickpire

⑫ Which pigment is found at the reaction centre?

The light-dependent stage of photosynthesis

The reactions of the light-dependent stage occur in the thylakoids of the chloroplasts. They involve:

- Photolysis, the splitting of water molecules by light to produce hydrogen ions and electrons.
- The synthesis of ATP from ADP and Pi. This type of phosphorylation is known as photophosphorylation, as light energy is involved.
- The combination of hydrogen ions with NADP to produce reduced NADP.

When light strikes a molecule at the reaction centre an electron is raised to a higher energy level, thus setting up a flow of electrons. This electron flow is referred to as the 'Z scheme'.

There are two ways in which ATP can be synthesised:

- Non-cyclic photophosphorylation.
- Cyclic photophosphorylation.

Non-cyclic photophosphorylation involves both photosystem I and photosystem II:

- Photons of light are absorbed by photosystem II and passed to chlorophyll a in the reaction centre.
- This causes the displacement of two 'excited' (high energy) electrons which are raised to a higher energy level where they are picked up by electron acceptors. These electron acceptors pass the electrons along a chain of carriers through a proton pump and to photosystem I.
- The energy lost by the electrons is used to convert ADP to ATP.
- Photons of light are absorbed by photosystem I and passed to chlorophyll a.
- This in turn causes two electrons to be emitted and raised to a higher energy level where they are picked up by another electron acceptor.
- Photosystem II is now unstable as it has lost electrons. These are replaced when electrons become available from the splitting of water by photolysis.
- During photolysis, the water molecule dissociates into electrons, hydrogen ions and oxygen.
- The second electron acceptor, which receives electrons from photosystem I, passes some of these electrons to hydrogen ions on the outside of the thylakoid membrane, where they reduce NADP.
- Since these electrons are not recycled back into the chlorophyll, this method of ATP production is called non-cyclic photophosphorylation.

quicKfire

⑬ What is the source of replacement electrons for photosystem II?

>> Pointer

Textbooks differ in their use of the term 'reduced NADP'. Some use $NADPH_2$, others $NADPH+H^+$.
Throughout this book the term 'reduced NADP' will be used.

quicKfire

⑭ What is the waste product of photosynthesis?

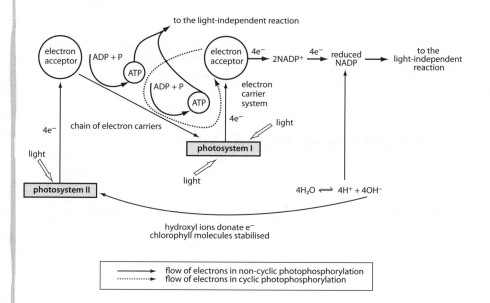

Z scheme.

⑮ State two differences between non-cyclic and cyclic photophosphorylation.

Grade boost

Compare chemiosmosis in photosynthesis with that in respiration.

Grade boost

The carrier system in photosynthesis has only one proton pump but in respiration there are three.

>> *Pointer*

The sequence of events in the light-dependent stage of photosynthesis was worked out by Calvin and his associates using C14, a radioisotope of carbon, and the unicellular algae, *Chlorella*. It is known as the Calvin cycle.

Cyclic photophosphorylation involves only photosystem I:

- Light energy is absorbed by PSI and passed to chlorophyll a at the reaction centre.
- The electrons are passed to a higher energy level where they are received by the second electron acceptor.
- Those electrons which are not taken up in the production of reduced NADP then pass along a chain of electron carriers before they are returned to PSI.
- As the electron passes along the chain of carriers, sufficient energy is generated to make ATP.
- No reduced NADP is produced during this process.

The reactions of the light-dependent stage of photosynthesis take place in the thylakoid membranes of the chloroplast. As electrons flow along the chain of electron carriers from photosystem II to photosystem I, they provide energy to pump hydrogen ions from the stroma, across the thylakoid membrane and into the thylakoid space. This sets up an electrochemical gradient, since there are more hydrogen ions inside the thylakoid space than there are outside in the stroma. Hydrogen ions flow along this gradient out across the thylakoid membrane through the protein channels. This produces energy sufficient for the formation of ATP by ATP synthetase.

The ATP and reduced NADP produced from the light-dependent stage are used in the light-independent stage.

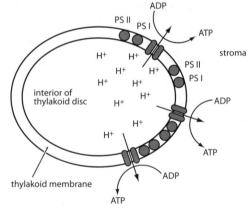

ATP production in the chloroplast by chemiosmosis.

The light-independent stage

The light-independent stage occurs in the stroma of the chloroplast and involves many reactions each catalysed by a different enzyme. The reactions use the products of the light-dependent stage, i.e. ATP as a source of energy, and reduced NADP as the source of the reducing power to reduce carbon dioxide and synthesise hexose sugar.

- A five-carbon acceptor molecule, ribulose bisphosphate (RuBP), combines with carbon dioxide (catalysed by the enzyme Rubisco) forming an unstable six-carbon compound.
- The six-carbon compound immediately splits into two molecules of a three-carbon compound called glycerate-3-phosphate (GP).
- GP is phosphorylated by ATP and then reduced by reduced NADP to triose phosphate.

- Some of this three-carbon sugar can be built up into glucose phosphate and then into starch by condensation.
- In order that the cycle continues, most of the triose phosphate formed enters a series of reactions driven by ATP which results in the regeneration of RuBP.
- The NADP is reformed and goes back to the light-dependent reaction to be reduced again.

Calvin cycle.

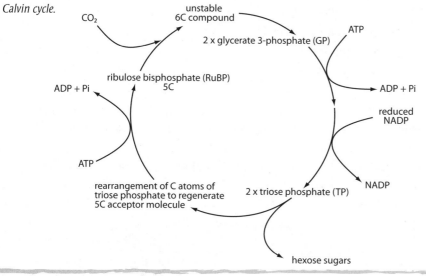

Grade boost

The Calvin cycle often appears on an exam paper and candidates find it difficult to memorise the intermediates of the cycle.

Grade boost

For every six molecules of triose phosphate formed, five are used to regenerate ribulose bisphosphate.

⑯ Why is it essential to regenerate ribulose bisphosphate?

Product synthesis

With the metabolism of triose phosphate to carbohydrates, lipids and amino acids and the absorption of mineral ions from the soil, the plant is able to manufacture all the other products needed for life.

Various inorganic nutrients are needed by plants and may be limiting factors to metabolism if in short supply. Mineral ions are also required for the synthesis of compounds needed for the growth of the plant.

Macronutrients, e.g. potassium, sodium, magnesium, calcium, nitrate and phosphate, are required in substantial quantities but the micronutrients, e.g. manganese and copper, are needed in much smaller amounts.

Nitrogen is taken up by the roots as nitrates. It is transported as nitrates in the xylem and as amino acids in the phloem. It is used for the synthesis of proteins and nucleic acids. Symptoms of nitrogen deficiency are reduced growth of all organs, and chlorosis, a yellowing of the leaves due to inadequate chlorophyll production. Chlorosis first appears in the older leaves.

Magnesium is absorbed as Mg++ and its function is in chlorophyll production and activation of ATPase. Magnesium is required by all tissues but especially leaves and is transported as Mg++ in the xylem.

Magnesium forms part of the chlorophyll molecule. Pronounced chlorosis begins between the veins of older leaves and is the main symptom of magnesium deficiency. This is because existing magnesium in the plant is mobilised and transported to newly formed leaves.

Pointer

You are not required to provide chemical details of the manufacture of the products of photosynthesis.

Pointer

You are not required to study other minerals, apart from nitrogen and magnesium.

>> *Pointer*

Micro-organisms include the groups: bacteria, fungi, viruses and Protoctista.

quickfire

⑰ What is the shape of a *Streptococcus* bacterium?

Grade boost

Apart from shape, further differentiation is often possible according to the way bacteria tend to be grouped, e.g. in pairs; forming chains; in clusters. The filamentous bacteria are of particular interest because most are photosynthetic. This group, formerly called blue-green algae, are now known as Cyanobacteria.

quickfire

⑱ What additional chemical is present in the cell wall of Gram-negative bacteria?

quickfire

⑲ What colour would Gram-negative bacteria stain with the Gram stain?

Microbiology

Classification

There are two main ways of classifying bacteria:

- By shape – bacteria may be:
  - Bacillus or rod shaped.
  - Cocci or spherical.
  - Spirillum or corkscrew shaped.
- By the Gram stain reaction – this enables microbiologists to distinguish between Gram-positive and Gram-negative bacteria. The different staining properties are due to differences in the chemical composition of their cell walls.

The cell wall consists of a mixture of polysaccharide and polypeptides, known as peptidoglycan or murein. The cross-linking provides strength, and gives the cell its shape, and the wall protects against swelling and bursting (lysis) due to osmosis.

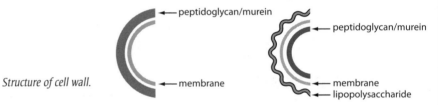

Structure of cell wall.

- Gram-negative bacteria have more chemically complex walls where the peptidoglycan is supplemented by large molecules of lipopolysaccharide which protect the cell. They do not retain dyes like crystal violet, and appear red or pink when viewed under the microscope. Gram-negative bacteria include *Salmonella* species. They are not affected by the antibacterial enzyme, lysozyme, which occurs in human tears, and are resistant to penicillin.
- Gram-positive bacteria lack the lipopolysaccharide in their walls and do retain crystal violet. They appear violet or purple under the microscope. These are more susceptible to antibiotics and the enzyme, lysozyme, than Gram-negative bacteria. Gram-positive bacteria include *Bacillus, Staphylococcus and Streptococcus* species.

Conditions necessary for growth

Micro-organisms reproduce quickly given a suitable environment. For example, bacteria are able to divide every twenty minutes under optimum conditions. In the laboratory, bacteria can be grown on a wide variety of substrates providing they are supplied with suitable physical conditions, nutrients and water. Micro-organisms vary in their requirements and usually grow over a range of temperatures and pH values, with an optimum within the range.

Micro-organisms require the following conditions for growth:

- Nutrients – in the laboratory nutrients are supplied in nutrient media, such as agar, and include carbon, usually in the form of glucose; nitrogen, in organic and inorganic form; growth factors such as vitamins and mineral salts. Nitrogen is needed to produce amino acids during protein synthesis.

- Temperature – as all growth is normally regulated by enzymes, the range of 25–45°C is favourable for the majority of bacteria. The optimum for mammalian pathogens is around 37°C.

- pH – most bacteria are favoured by slightly alkaline conditions (pH 7.4), whereas fungi prefer neutral to slightly acid conditions.

- Oxygen – many micro-organisms require oxygen for metabolism and are termed obligate aerobes. Some, while growing better in the presence of oxygen, can nevertheless survive in its absence; these are called facultative anaerobes. Others cannot grow in the presence of oxygen and are called obligate anaerobes. *Clostridium* bacteria are obligate anaerobes that produce toxins or poisons in a wound. These bacteria destroy body tissue and the condition is called moist gangrene.

Principles of aseptic technique

Bacteria (and fungi) are cultured on, or in, media that are designed to supply the cell with all its nutritional requirements. Aseptic techniques (also known as sterile techniques), in which the apparatus and equipment are kept free of micro-organisms, are used to prevent contamination of bacterial cultures and the surrounding environment.

- To prevent the contamination of pure cultures and apparatus by bacteria from the environment:
  - Sterilise all apparatus and media before use to prevent initial contamination.
  - Handle cultures carefully and use equipment such as sterile loops to prevent subsequent contamination.

- To prevent contamination to the environment by the bacteria being used in experiments:
  - Sterilise the work surface before and after an experiment using a disinfectant, e.g. Lysol used as a 3% solution.
  - Use the correct handling techniques to prevent the contamination of personnel and the immediate environment by the organisms being cultured.

For example, when carrying out the process of inoculation:

- Grasp the culture bottle in one hand; remove the cap with the little finger of the other hand – do not place the cap down on the work surface.
- Flame the mouth of the bottle for 2 or 3 seconds.
- Pass the inoculating loop through a flame until red hot.
- Lift the lid of the petri dish just enough to allow entry of the inoculating loop.

>> **Pointer**

Two potential problems which must be prevented when working with bacteria are the prevention of contamination of the supplied cultures from the environment and the prevention of contamination to the environment.

quickfire

20 Apart from oxygen list three other requirements for microbial growth.

>> **Pointer**

All organisms including micro-organisms use enzymes. Consider this when describing their growth and reproduction and also how they may be destroyed.

Key term

Pathogen = a disease-causing microbe.

Grade boost

An examiner will be impressed if you can incorporate your practical experience into your exam answers and be aware of the safety issues and potential hazards associated with practical techniques.

Grade boost

Would you be able to answer this exam essay? 'Outline the aseptic techniques that are needed for handling micro-organisms in the laboratory?'

quickfire

㉑ Why should petri dishes containing bacterial cultures not be incubated at body temperature?

Grade boost

Under certain unfavourable growth conditions a few bacteria such as *Clostridium*, are capable of producing an internal resting cell known as an endospore. This is a means of protecting the nuclear material. Endospores are resistant to heat, drying, pH change and disinfectants. When favourable conditions return they can form a bacterial cell.

quickfire

㉒ Why is it necessary to sterilise equipment at a temperature of 121°C for 15 minutes?

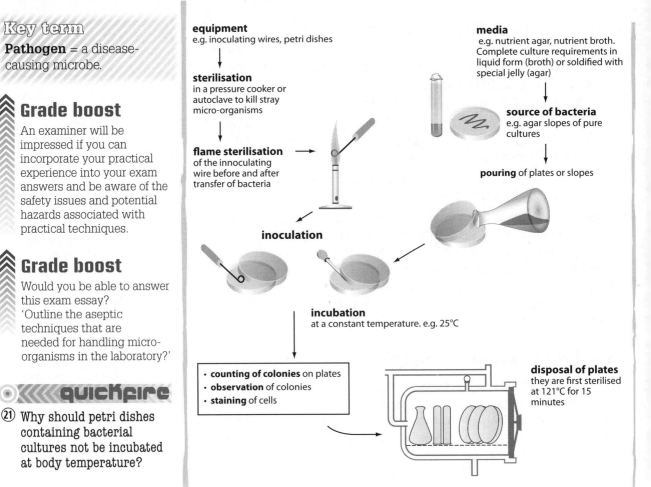

equipment
e.g. inoculating wires, petri dishes

sterilisation
in a pressure cooker or autoclave to kill stray micro-organisms

flame sterilisation
of the innoculating wire before and after transfer of bacteria

inoculation

media
e.g. nutrient agar, nutrient broth. Complete culture requirements in liquid form (broth) or soldified with special jelly (agar)

source of bacteria
e.g. agar slopes of pure cultures

pouring of plates or slopes

incubation
at a constant temperature. e.g. 25°C

- **counting of colonies** on plates
- **observation** of colonies
- **staining** of cells

disposal of plates
they are first sterilised at 121°C for 15 minutes

Sterile techniques.

– Secure the petri dish lid with adhesive tape. Use two pieces of tape to fasten the lid, but do not seal all the way round as this could create anaerobic conditions and encourage the growth of possible **pathogenic** micro-organisms.

– Incubate at around 25°C (cultures should not be cultured at 37°C as this is an ideal temperature for the growth of many pathogenic species).

– Do not open petri dishes after incubation.

• In a laboratory the preferred method of sterilisation is to use an autoclave. This is a sealed container in which glass and metal equipment is heated at 121°C in steam under pressure for 15 minutes after the required pressure has been reached. This ensures that any resistant endospores are destroyed, e.g. Gram-positive bacteria such as *Clostridium* are resistant to boiling.

• Disposable materials, such as plastic petri dishes, can be sealed inside autoclavable plastic bags and placed in a dustbin after having been autoclaved.

• Radiation, e.g. gamma rays, is used commercially to sterilise plastic equipment.

Methods of measuring growth

The size of a population of micro-organisms in liquid culture may be measured by counting cells directly, or by taking some indirect method such as the turbidity (cloudiness) of the culture. Direct cell counts may be divided into:

- Total counts, which include both living and dead cells.
- Viable counts, which count living cells only.

In practice, it is never possible to count whole populations of micro-organisms. Instead, the cells in a very small sample of culture are counted, and the result multiplied up to give a population density in organisms per cm^3 of culture. Even then the population density is likely to be so high that cell counts are usually made in known dilutions of the culture, usually in 10-fold steps. This is known as serial dilution.

There are several different methods of measuring growth:

- Measuring growth directly. Rough estimates of growth rates can be made by regularly measuring the diameter of a bacterial or fungal **colony** as it spreads from a central point to cover the surface of a solid growth medium. This is known as the dilution plating technique.

- Serial dilution technique. A culture medium, such as milk, is made into a series of dilutions using the A sample, $1cm^3$, is streaked onto a sterile agar plate which is then placed in an incubator at 25°C for two days. After all the streaks have been allowed to grow, the dilution at which the colonies are distinct and separate is counted. (If the dilution is insufficient then colonies will merge, referred to as 'clumping', and counting is inaccurate.)

Serial dilution.

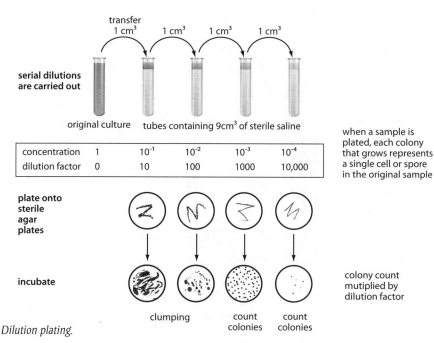

Dilution plating.

Key term

Colony (of bacteria) = a cluster of cells or clone which arises from a single bacterium by asexual reproduction.

Grade boost

Estimating the growth of bacteria is extremely important. Environmental health officers regularly inspect food premises and take samples for analysis. Water boards check water supplies daily. Many products are produced using bacteria grown in fermenters. Measuring their growth is an important part of the process.

quickfire

㉓ What assumption is made when counting colonies?

quickfire

㉔ By what process does one cell give rise to a colony?

>> *Pointer*

You are not required to describe or use a haemocytometer or colorimeter.

quickfire

㉕ State three advantages of using industrial fermenters.

⚑ **Grade boost**

Primary metabolism is the norm, when the fungus is metabolising glucose to release energy and increasing its own biomass. Continuous cultivation is suitable for products known as primary metabolites. This allows production to continue for much longer, as nutrients are added throughout the process and the products are continuously being removed. Many products including alcohol and insulin are produced in this way.

quickfire

㉖ Why is ammonia included as one of the nutrients?

- The separate colonies of bacteria are counted with the assumption being made that each colony has arisen from a single cell, which has divided asexually, from the original medium. To find the total viable cell count the number of colonies is multiplied by the appropriate dilution factor. This method makes no allowance for clumping of cells so may cause an underestimate of numbers.

- Using a haemocytometer. This is a more accurate method using a specialised microscope slide. Using the haemocytometer gives total cell counts as it is not possible to distinguish between living and dead cells.

- Turbidimetry. A colorimeter is used to measure the cloudiness or turbidity of the culture as cell numbers increase. Results are derived by comparison with a standard graph of light absorbance plotted against known cell numbers.

Batch culture fermentation

Industrial fermentation is widely used to culture bacterial and fungal cells. An important use of large-scale industrial fermentation is the production of antibiotics such as penicillin.

There are a number of advantages to using micro-organisms in fermentation. The microbes grow rapidly and enzymes do not have to be supplied. This means that fermentation can take place at lower temperatures than normally used in industrial processes and therefore production is cheaper.

Batch fermenter.

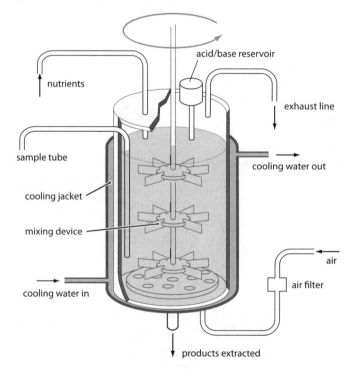

Fermenter design

The following describes the main principles of batch fermentation:

- A pure culture of an organism is needed for the formation and harvesting of a pure product during and after growth in a fermenter vessel. The organism must be supplied with suitable conditions for growth and without competition for maximum efficiency.

- The vessel should be sterilised beforehand and an appropriate sterile medium used. During use the vessel openings must be protected from contamination by filters, and aseptic conditions and handling are required to maintain purity.

- Forced aeration may be needed, for maximum growth of aerobes, which may also mix the culture to improve contact with nutrients. Mixing may be improved by a separate mixer.

- Temperature monitoring and control are required to maintain constant conditions and water-jackets remove excess heat produced during the culture process.

- Commercially, sophisticated monitors are used to improve control of temperature and pH, and air inlets may use spargers or other devices to improve aeration.

Production of penicillin

- The fermenter is inoculated with a culture of *Penicillium notatum*, which then grows under the optimum conditions provided in the fermenter.

- It takes about 30 hours for penicillin production to begin. The penicillin is secreted by the fungus and accumulates in the medium. The delay in production occurs because penicillin is a **secondary metabolite**.

- After about six days the culture fluid mixture is filtered and the penicillin is extracted and purified. That is, the culture medium, after filtering, is retained and processed.

- This type of fermentation is known as a batch culture. The fermenter has to be emptied, cleaned and sterilised, ready for the next batch.

Antibiotic production is an example of secondary metabolism, i.e. the antibiotic is produced at a period in the life of the fungus when there is a change away from its optimum conditions. This reflects the need for the organism, when free living, to reduce competition when food sources are depleted.

Graph showing growth of Penicillium and yield of antobiotic.

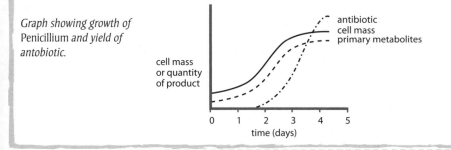

Key term
Secondary metabolite
= a chemical which is not necessary for the growth of the fungus and is produced after the exponential phase of growth is completed, when glucose is depleted.

》 Pointer
Candidates often describe the components of a fermenter without giving their function.

Grade boost
A common error when describing the production of penicillin is to state that a bacterium is used in its production. Candidates should state that the fungus, *Penicillium*, is used in the process.

 **quickfire**
㉗ Why is the cooling jacket essential to the process?

quickfire
㉘ Why does the fungus produce antibiotic when glucose is depleted?

Key terms

Birth rate = the reproductive capacity of the population.

Emigration = the movement of individuals out of a population.

Immigration = the movement of individuals into a population.

Population = a group of organisms of a single species interbreeding and occupying a particular area.

Grade boost

The S-shaped curve is typical of any species that colonises new habitats. There is a period of slow growth as the species adapts to the habitat, followed by a period of rapid growth with little environmental resistance. The graph then levels off as the population reaches its carrying capacity. If one factor becomes in short supply, then this can limit the growth of the population, which then goes into decline.

quickfire

㉙ Explain the reason for the lag phase during population growth.

Populations

Factors controlling population growth

The growth of a particular **population** at a particular time is determined by the **birth rate** and death rate. In addition, individuals can **immigrate** to or **emigrate** from an area. The following describes what happens when a species colonises a new area under favourable conditions:

1. The lag phase – this may last from a few minutes to several days. There is little cell multiplication or growth. (As only a few individuals are present initially the rate of growth is very slow.) This is a period of adaptation or preparation for growth, with intense metabolic activity, notably enzyme synthesis.

2. The exponential phase – as numbers increase, providing there is no factor limiting growth, more individuals become available for reproduction. In the case of bacteria the cells begin to divide at a constant rate with the population doubling per unit time. The cell population increases geometrically. This rate of increase cannot be maintained indefinitely.

3. The stationary phase – population growth enters this phase when the birth rate of new individuals is equal to the death rate of older ones. Certain factors limit the population growth. The population has reached its maximum size. This is known as the carrying capacity for the particular environment in which the population occurs. This describes the limit to the number of individuals that an area can support.

4. The death phase – when death rate is greater than birth rate. This may occur when all the food in a nutrient solution has been used up.

Environmental resistance includes all the factors that may limit the growth of a population. These factors include available food, predation, parasitism, disease, overcrowding, competition, accumulation of toxic waste, weather. Thus, population growth slows down due to environmental resistance.

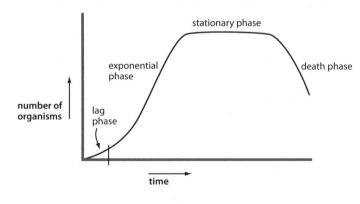

Graph showing changes in population growth.

Factors that regulate population increase

It is possible to distinguish between those factors that will slow down population growth rate and those that might cause a population crash:

- Some factors are density dependent, that is, their effect increases as the density of the population increases. For example, accumulation of toxic waste, disease, parasitism and depletion of food supply. The carrying capacity is dependent on the resources provided by the environment (which therefore act as density-dependent factors).

- Other factors are density independent. The effect of these factors does not depend on the population density. All the plants and animals are affected no matter what the population size. The effect is the same regardless of the size of the population. It is usually due to a sudden or violent change in an abiotic factor, e.g. freezing, flood or fire.

Populations fluctuate in numbers

In general, the size of a population is regulated by the balance between the birth rate and the death rate. However, populations fluctuate; they do not remain constant in size, although these fluctuations are not usually large and erratic. The numbers of most species lie near an equilibrium point known as the set point. For a given species in a particular environment, there is a certain equilibrium population that the environment can support. If the population rises above the set point, a density-dependent factor increases mortality or reduces breeding to such an extent that the population declines.

If the population falls below the set point, environmental resistance is temporarily relieved so that the population rises again.

The size of a population may fluctuate on a regular basis. This may be the consequence of weather patterns such as temperature or rainfall.

Population oscillations are regulated by a process known as negative feedback.

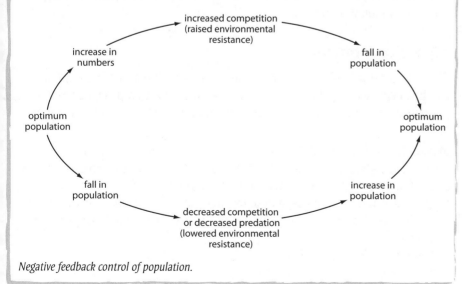

Negative feedback control of population.

quickfire

③⓪ What is meant by the term 'carrying capacity'?

quickfire

③① Distinguish between density-dependent and density-independent factors.

quickfire

③② List three density-dependent factors that may limit the growth of a population.

Grade boost

Occasionally it is reported that there is a population explosion of organisms such as greenfly. This may be due to a decrease in the number of their predators or may be due to an increase in weather patterns. These fluctuations will self-regulate by negative feedback.

Key terms

Insecticides = chemicals used to kill insects.

Pest = any organism that competes with or adversely affects a population of organisms that are of economic importance.

Pesticides = poisonous chemicals used to control organisms considered harmful to agriculture or organisms involved in disease transmission.

Resistance = the ability of an organism to survive exposure to a dose of that poison which would normally be lethal to it.

Grade boost

To avoid confusing the terms 'intraspecific' and 'interspecific' think of the intranet within an organisation and the internet between organisations.

quickfire

㉝ When two species of a single-celled organism, *Paramecium*, *P. aurelia* and *P. caudatum* were grown together in a culture, what type of competition is most likely to have caused the numbers of *P. caudatum* to decrease?

Competition

In nature, plants and animals have to struggle to survive. Plants compete for resources such as light, space, water and nutrients. Animals compete for food, shelter, space and reproductive partners. There are two types of competition:

- Intraspecific competition is competition between individuals of the same species. This type of competition is density dependent since, as the population increases, a greater proportion of the population fails to survive. This has value to a population, since organisms tend to produce more offspring than the habitat can support. Those organisms that are best adapted have a better chance of survival.

- Interspecific competition is competition between individuals of different species. Each species occupies a particular place, or niche, in an ecosystem. This is not only the particular physical space it occupies but also the role it carries out within the community. In the long term, two species cannot occupy the same niche in a specific habitat.

Pest control

Pests attack crop plants and animals causing a reduction in yield and a massive economic loss for farmers. Pests:

- feed on crops and animals
- compete with crop organisms for resources
- can directly cause disease in crop organisms
- can make infection by pathogens more likely
- can spoil food when it is being stored or transported.

When pest numbers are causing so much damage then it becomes worth spending money on controlling the pest. The farmer has the option of using chemical or biological control.

Chemical control

Chemical control involves using **pesticides** and includes herbicides, fungicides and **insecticides**. The chemicals can be sprayed onto the crop, applied as powders or smokes in enclosed areas, sprayed onto animals or added to animal feed.

Ideally an insecticide should be specific, non-persistent and should not accumulate and be passed along food chains. Organochlorine chemicals, such as DDT, were persistent and remained in the environment for long periods, a property which is regarded as undesirable in a modern pesticide. The overuse of pesticides has also led to the development of **resistance** among many species of insects.

Advantages and disadvantages of chemical control

Advantages

- It is a very effective means of control.
- Pests are eradicated quickly and relatively cheaply.
- Chemicals can be applied on a small scale, such as to a single field.
- Application does not require a high level of skill.

Disdvantages

- The chemicals are not specific and can eradicate beneficial insects. For example, pollinating insects, such as bees, biological control agents. With the removal of the insect predators of the pest there may be a resurgence (build-up in numbers) of the pest.
- Pests may become resistant to the pesticide.
- Some pesticides may kill fish, birds or mammals by contaminating their food, e.g. seed dressings.
- Long-term over-exposure to pesticides can cause harm to humans, for example farmers using sheep dips.

Biological control

- A specific type of interspecific competition involves the relationship between the predator and its prey.
- Predators kill other animals (their prey) for food. Predators are normally larger than their prey and tend to kill before they eat. The abundance of prey is a factor limiting the numbers of the predator. Within a food chain, a predator–prey relationship causes both populations to oscillate and these oscillations are regulated by **negative feedback**.
- The effect of the predator–prey relationship in regulating populations has been exploited by humans as a method of controlling pests. That is, biological control methods exploit natural enemies to regulate the population of pest species. A beneficial organism (the agent) is deployed against an undesirable one (the target). The aim is to reduce the pest population to a tolerable level by artificially increasing the populations of the agent. That is, to keep the numbers of the pest below the economic damage threshold for a particular crop. To eradicate the pest completely could be counter-productive. This would not leave any food source for the predator, which would then die out. Should the pest re-invade at a later date it would soon increase its numbers to an economically damaging level.
- Some of the most successful results have been achieved using insect parasites. More recently, micro-organisms have been used as specific insect pathogens.
- Pests are normally regulated by their natural predators. Modern agriculture can upset the natural system. For example, where the requirement for larger field has resulted in destruction of hedgerows and has reduced the natural

Key term

Negative feedback = when there is a change in a monitored variable, a response is triggered to counteract the initial fluctuation.

quickfire

㉞ List the properties of an ideal insecticide.

③⑤ List the properties of an organism used for biological control of a pest.

③⑥ A parasitic wasp, *Encarsia formosa*, may be used to control whitefly populations in a glasshouse. State two reasons why it would be inappropriate to use both chemical and biological methods at the same time.

Grade boost

A favourite essay question asks the candidate to describe the advantages and disadvantages of chemical and biological control.

habitat of predators. Some of the most successful examples of biological control concern insects introduced from another country. However, in some cases these insects have subsequently become serious pests in their new habitat. When their native predators or parasites have then also been introduced, the pest problem has crashed spectacularly.

Advantages and disadvantages of biological control

Advantages

- It is usually highly specific to one pest. That is, it must target the pest only.
- It can provide long-term control if population equilibrium is established.
- Initial research costs mean that it is expensive to introduce. However, biological control is relatively inexpensive in the long term.
- There is no environmental contamination.
- It can be used in the glasshouse situation.

Disadvantages

- Biological control agents are slow to build up in number to react to a sudden increase in pest numbers.
- Successful examples are relatively few in number; agents are not known for most pest problems.
- Success usually involves a high level of skill and research. This can be expensive.
- A detailed knowledge of the life cycle is required. There is the potential for the release of exotic organisms with unknown ecological effects. (There have been examples where the predator, having eradicated the pest, has turned to an alternative food supply and has itself become a pest.)
- A frequent input is needed to attain a population balance.
- Apart from glasshouse pests, it is of little use to individual producers as introduction needs to be carried out on a large scale.

Integrated pest control

Despite the development of improved pesticides such as organophosphates and synthetic pyrethroids, it is now considered that pest control is best achieved by combining various methods. These include the use of biological control agents, producing pest-resistant crops, varying cultivation techniques and, where necessary, the minimal, well-targeted application of highly selective pesticides. This is known as integrated pest management.

Recycling nutrients

Carbon cycle

The basis of the carbon cycle involves:

- Carbon dioxide is added to the air by the respiration of animals, plants and micro-organisms and by the combustion of fossil fuels.
- Photosynthesis takes place on so great a scale that it re-uses on a daily basis almost as much carbon dioxide as is released into the atmosphere.
- The production of carbohydrates, proteins and fats contributes to plant growth and subsequently to animal growth through complex food webs. The dead remains of plants and animals are then acted upon by **saprobionts** in the soil, which ultimately release gaseous CO_2 back to the atmosphere.

Globally the level of carbon dioxide has increased. The main reason for this increase is two human activities:

- The burning of fossil fuels has released to the atmosphere carbon dioxide that was previously locked up within these fuels.
- Deforestation has removed large quantities of photosynthesising biomass and so less carbon dioxide is being removed from the atmosphere.

Carbon cycle.

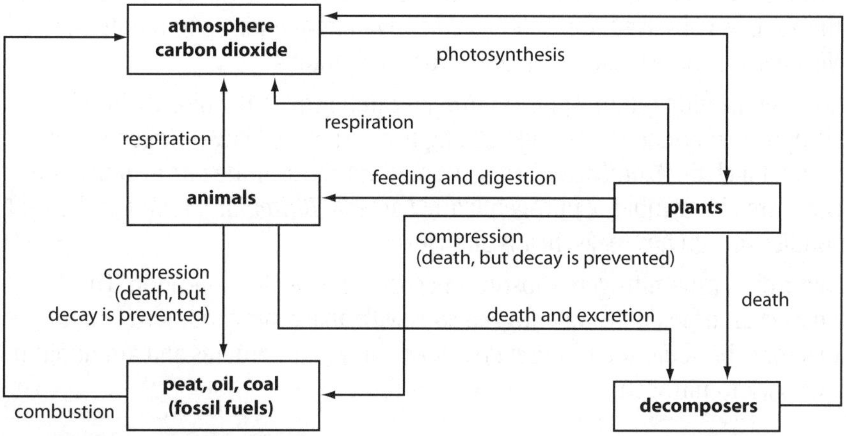

The nitrogen cycle

The nitrogen cycle is the flow of organic and inorganic nitrogen within an ecosystem where there is an interchange between nitrogenous compounds and atmospheric nitrogen.

Living organisms need nitrogen to make amino acids, proteins and nucleic acids. Plants and animals are unable to use nitrogen gas. Instead plants take in nitrates in solution through their roots. The organic nitrogen compounds produced by plants are transferred through the food chain when consumers eat plants. When plants and animals die the minerals locked in their bodies, together with the excretory products of animals, must be decomposed in order to release the minerals back into the soil.

Key term

Saprobiont (also saprophyte) = a micro-organism that obtains its food from the dead or decaying remains of other organisms.

Pointer

In the distant past large quantities of dead organisms accumulated in anaerobic conditions and so were prevented from decaying. In time they formed coal, oil and other fossil fuels.

Pointer

The topic 'deforestation' is studied in BY5.

quickfire

㊲ Explain the rise of carbon dioxide levels in the atmosphere.

Grade boost

Nitrogen is found in all amino acids and the proteins which are formed from them. Nitrogen is taken up by plants through the roots as nitrate ions.

quickfire

㊳ Explain why plants require nitrate.

Pointer

Bacteria are the key organisms involved in the nitrogen cycle.

Grade boost

When plants and animals die, valuable minerals are released in a form that can be absorbed by plants and so contribute to recycling. The organisms, which include fungi and bacteria, are called decomposers.

Grade boost

Candidates find difficulty in understanding the nitrogen cycle. It may help to build up your own diagram and use different colours for each process rather than using a prepared diagram.

quickfire

39 Give the term for the process of converting ammonium ions to nitrate ions.

Grade boost

You must learn the specific names of the bacteria involved in the nitrogen cycle.

quickfire

40 Suggest one way in which total nitrogen can be lost from an area of land.

Grade boost

Draining land and ploughing fields ensure that anaerobic bacteria cannot compete with aerobic bacteria thus preventing denitrification.

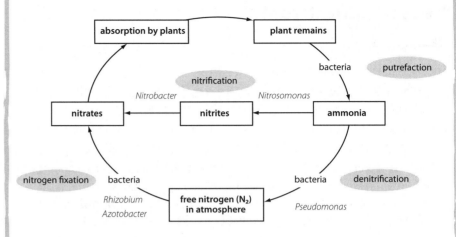

Nitrogen cycle.

The main processes involved are as follows:

- Putrefaction – bacteria, and fungi are called decomposers and result in the decay of dead plants and animals, faeces and urine into ammonium ions. This process is also called ammonification.

- Nitrification – the ammonia formed in putrefaction is converted by nitrification via nitrites to nitrates. Various bacteria are involved. For example, ammonia is converted to nitrite by *Nitrosomonas* and nitrite to nitrate by *Nitrobacter*. These bacteria require aerobic conditions.

- Nitrogen fixation – atmospheric nitrogen can be converted directly into nitrogen compounds by nitrogen fixing bacteria. Free living nitrogen fixing bacteria include *Azotobacter*. These account for most of the nitrogen fixation. There are also symbiotic nitrogen fixing bacteria, *Rhizobium*, found in the root nodules of legumes (peas, beans and clover).

- Denitrification – nitrogen is lost from ecosystems by denitrification. This is a particular problem in waterlogged soils with anaerobic conditions where anaerobic bacteria, such as *Pseudomonas*, can reduce nitrates and ammonium ions back to nitrogen.

Human activities can improve nitrogen circulation

- By fixing atmospheric nitrogen artificially using chemical processes that convert it to fertilisers.
- Large amount of animal waste from stock rearing is used as manure.
- Sewage disposal boosts organic nitrogen supplies.
- Micro-organisms can be used for making compost and silage.
- Farming practices such as:
  - Planting fields of clover to encourage nitrogen fixation.
  - Draining land and reducing anaerobic conditions.
  - Ploughing fields in order to improve aeration of the soil.

Control systems co-ordinate and regulate processes

Homeostasis

Homeostasis means the maintenance of a constant environment within a living organism. Examples of homeostatic control systems include: maintaining constant blood glucose levels, thermoregulation, osmoregulation function of the kidney.

The control of any self-regulating system involves a series of stages that feature the set point, which is the desired level at which the system operates. This is monitored by:

- A sensor, which detects any deviation from the set point.

- When the receptor detects a change from the norm it sends instructions to a co-ordinator.

- The co-ordinator communicates with one or more effectors which carry out the corrective procedures.

- Once the correction is made and the factor returned to normal, information is fed back to the detector which then 'switches off'.

- This is what happens in most biological control systems, i.e. the co-ordinator is no longer alerted to the deviation from the normal. This is called a **negative feedback.**

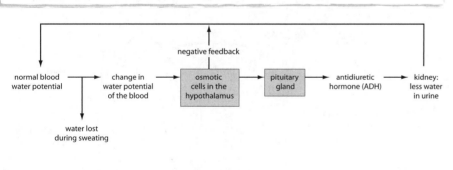

Feedback loop.

The kidney

The kidney performs two main functions:

- Removal of nitrogenous metabolic waste from the body.

- Osmoregulation, the mechanism by which the balance of water and dissolved solutes is regulated.

Key term

Negative feedback = a series of changes, that result in a substance being restored to its normal level.

quickfire

㊶ Why is negative feedback important in maintaining a system at a set point?

quickfire

㊷ With reference to the diagram:
  (a) Which of the structures acts as:
    (i) a receptor
    (ii) an effector?
  (b) How is ADH transported to the kidney?

Production of urea

Urea is a poisonous chemical made by the liver. If there is too much protein in the diet, any excess has to be broken down (as it cannot be stored like carbohydrates and fats). The amino acids, which make up protein, are deaminated in the liver. The reaction produces ammonia, which is quickly converted to urea. Urea is released into the blood, and travels around the body until it is removed by the kidneys.

Structure of the kidney

Humans have two kidneys and these are the main organs that filter waste products from the blood.

Each kidney is made up of about a million uriniferous tubules or nephrons.

Within each Bowman's capsule is a knot of blood capillaries known as the glomerulus. The blood supply to the nephron begins as an afferent arteriole serving the glomerulus. From the glomerulus the blood is carried by the efferent arteriole to two other capillary structures:

- A capillary network serving the proximal and distal convoluted tubules.
- A capillary network running beside the loop of Henle and known as the vasa recta.

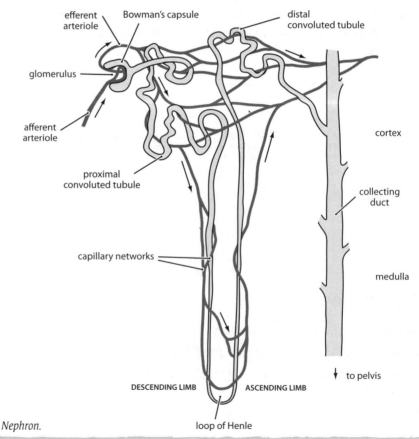

Nephron.

V.S. Kidney.

>> **Pointer**

In a practical activity you would be expected to interpret the histology of the kidney as seen in sections using the light microscope.

>> **Pointer**

The functioning of the nephron involves three different processes: ultrafiltration, selective reabsorption, secretion.

quickfire

43 Which region of the kidney contains the Bowman's capsules?

Ultrafiltration

Ultrafiltration is a filtration under pressure that separates small soluble molecules from the blood plasma. It is the process by which small molecules such as water, glucose, urea and salts are filtered from the knot of capillaries, the glomerulus, into the Bowman's capsule. The blood entering the glomerulus is separated from the space inside the Bowman's capsule by two cell layers and a basement membrane.

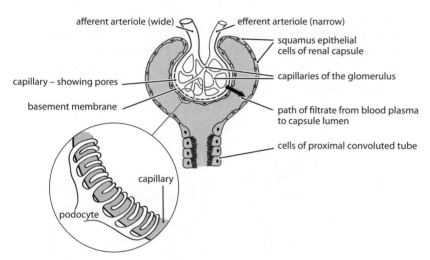

Bowman's capsule.

- The structure of the glomerulus and capsule allows ultrafiltration to take place. The basement membrane of the capillary forms the selective barrier between the blood and the nephron and it acts as a molecular sieve.
  - The first cell layer is the wall of the capillary. This single layer of cells contains many small gaps.
  - The basement membrane between the two cell layers acts as a filter during ultrafiltration.
  - The second cell layer makes up the wall of the Bowman's capsule. The epithelial cells in this layer are called podocytes.
- The sieve action allows smaller-sized molecules to pass through but retains in the capillaries the blood proteins and cells.
- Most of the pressure producing the filtration comes from the hydrostatic pressure of the blood in the glomerular capillaries. This pressure is amplified by the pressure in the capsule produced by the narrow efferent vessels and also by the water potential in the blood produced by the colloidal plasma proteins. The glomerular pressure can be altered by changes in the diameter of the afferent and efferent arterioles entering and leaving the glomerulus.

>> *Pointer*

You are expected to interpret the ultrastructure of the kidney: the arrangement of the pores in the Bowman's capsule in addition to the detail of cells from the wall of the proximal convoluted tubule.

(44) Explain the importance of the diameter of the efferent vessel being narrower than that of the afferent vessel.

» *Pointer*

Materials in the blood include blood cells, plasma proteins, glucose, salts, water, and urea. The blood cells and plasma proteins remain in the blood. All the glucose is reabsorbed into the blood. Most of the water and salts are also reabsorbed into the blood leaving urine, which is made up of urea with some water and salts, which passes to the bladder.

quickfire

(45) In what region of the uriniferous tubule is all of the glucose and most of the water and salt reabsorbed?

⤒ Grade boost

The counter-current multiplier mechanism is a difficult concept.

The end result is a low water potential at the apex of the loop. Collectively the large number of loops create a region of low water potential in the medulla and as the collecting ducts carrying urine pass through the medulla, water is drawn out by osmosis resulting in more concentrated urine. It thus acts as a 'fine control' of osmoregulation.

Selective reabsorption

Selective reabsorption is the process by which useful products such as glucose and salts are reabsorbed back into the blood as the filtrate flows along the nephron.

- All the glucose and most of the water and salt (sodium and chloride ions) are reabsorbed in the proximal convoluted tubule. Small amounts of water and salt are reabsorbed in the distal tubule. Most of the remaining water is reabsorbed in the collecting duct by a mechanism which involves the loop of Henle.

- Reabsorption of glucose and salts takes place by active transport. Water is reabsorbed passively by osmosis following the transport of salt.

- The loops of Henle collectively concentrate salts in the tissue fluid of the medulla of the kidney.

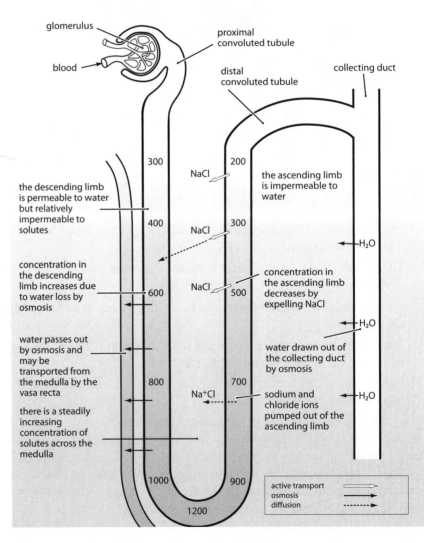

Counter-current multiplier.

- The high concentration of salt then causes an osmotic flow of water out of the collecting ducts thereby concentrating the urine and making it hypertonic to the blood.
- The loop of Henle uses the principle of a hair-pin counter-current multiplier.
- As fluid flows up the ascending limb, Na^+ and Cl^- are actively pumped out of the ascending limb into the tissue fluid of the surrounding medulla where a low water potential is created. The ascending limb is relatively impermeable to water, while the descending limb is permeable. Water leaves the filtrate of the descending limb by osmosis and is carried away by the blood in the vasa recta.
- The content of the descending limb becomes progressively more concentrated and reaches its maximum concentration at the tip of the loop; as it flows up the ascending limb the fluid becomes more and more dilute. Since the surrounding fluid also becomes more concentrated, an osmotic gradient is maintained down to the tip of the loop. The effect at one level is slight, but the overall effect is multiplied by the length of the hair-pin. The result is that a region of particularly high salt concentration is produced in a deep part of the medulla, resulting in the osmotic extraction of water from the adjacent permeable collecting ducts.
- The cells in the wall of the proximal convoluted tubule are adapted by having:
  - Microvilli providing a large surface area for absorption.
  - Numerous mitochondria providing ATP for active transport.

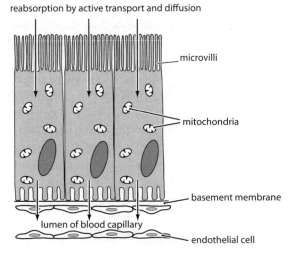

reabsorption by active transport and diffusion

microvilli

mitochondria

basement membrane

lumen of blood capillary

endothelial cell

Cells from the wall of the proximal convoluted tubule.

>> **Pointer**
Be prepared to draw selected cells in an exam question.

quickfire

46 State two ways in which the cells of the proximal convoluted tubules are adapted for absorption.

Key term

Osmoregulation = the homeostatic control of body water.

quickfire

(47) Name:
(a) the structure responsible for the detection of changes in the water potential of blood.
(b) the gland responsible for the release of ADH.

Grade boost

If blood has a lower water potential than the norm, the release of ADH and its effect on the permeability of the walls of the collecting duct and distal convoluted tubule results in water being drawn by osmosis from these areas towards the area of low water potential in the medulla where it passes into the blood.

Osmoregulation and the role of the posterior pituitary gland in the secretion of ADH

Mammals have to maintain a balance between water gain and water loss. Humans gain most of their water from drinking and from food. Most of the water is lost as urine. Other losses are due to sweating, keeping exchange surfaces moist, and loss in faeces.

- **Osmoregulation** operates on the principle of negative feedback, typical of homeostasis:
  - The receptors responsible for detecting changes are located in the hypothalamus, at the base of the brain.
  - The posterior lobe of pituitary acts as the co-ordinator.
  - The collecting ducts of kidney act as the effector.
- The permeability of the walls of the collecting duct, like the walls of the distal convoluted tubule, is subject to hormonal control. This hormonal effect, together with the hypertonic interstitial fluids built up by the loop of Henle in the medulla; determine whether hypotonic or hypertonic urine is released from the kidney.

ADH makes the walls of the collecting duct permeable so that water is reabsorbed and the urine has a concentration close to the concentration of the tissues near the bottom of the loop, that is, hypertonic to the general body fluids.

Water reabsorbed is controlled by a feedback system. Negative feedback restores the normal osmotic concentration if blood is diluted or becomes more concentrated.

A fall in water potential of the blood may be caused by one or a combination of factors – reduced water intake, sweating, intake of large amounts of salt. The concentration of sodium chloride in the blood is an indirect indication of the volume of water in the body. The hypothalamus is sensitive to the concentration of sodium chloride in the blood flowing through it. If the water content is low, a fall in water potential is detected by osmoreceptors (osmotic receptors) in the hypothalamus and results in nerve impulses passing to the posterior pituitary gland, which then releases ADH into the blood stream. This has the following effects:

- ADH increases the permeability of the distal convoluted tubule and the collecting duct to water.
- This allows more water to be reabsorbed from these tubules into the region of high solute concentration in the medulla.
- More water is reabsorbed into the blood.
- Consequently the small volume of urine eventually eliminated is relatively concentrated.

Adaptations to different environments

The environment in which an animal lives plays a part in the type of nitrogenous waste produced, and different animals deal with its disposal in different ways:

- Aquatic animals, such as fish, produce ammonia which, although highly toxic, is extremely soluble in water. The ammonia diffuses out across the gills and is quickly diluted to non-toxic levels.

- Birds and insects excrete uric acid which is almost insoluble in water and is non-toxic. There is a large energy cost to its production but very little water is needed for its excretion. This is important in conserving water and allows these organisms to live in dry environments.

- Mammals excrete urea. Its production also requires energy but it is less toxic than ammonia and so tissues can tolerate it in higher concentrations for relatively short periods of time.

Mammals have adapted the loop of Henle to enable them to live in arid areas such as deserts. The loop of Henle is concerned with water reabsorption. The longer the loop, the greater is the solute concentration in the medulla. This enables more water to be reabsorbed so the more concentrated is the urine. Mammals, such as the kangaroo rat, live in the desert and have particularly long loops of Henle.

Many desert animals survive with little or no water. How do they do this? They live on '**metabolic water**'. That is, water produced from the breakdown of food reserves during respiration in the cells. Many desert animals also remain underground during the day, living in burrows which are cool and humid, reducing water loss by evaporation.

Mammal	Habitat	Urine concentration (mOsmol l⁻¹)
Cat	Mesic	3100
Kangaroo rat	Desert	5500
Beaver	Freshwater	520

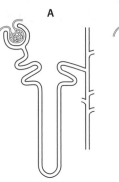

Nephrons from three different environments.

Key term
Metabolic water = water produced from the oxidation of food reserves.

quickfire

48 Which excretory product requires the least amount of water for its excretion?

quickfire

49 Using the information in the table identify the mammals to which the nephrons A to C belong.

>> *Pointer*

The cell bodies of sensory neurons are accommodated in a swelling called a ganglion.

Grade boost

You should remember the sequence: stimulus, receptor, sensory neurone, intermediate neurone, motor neurone, effector, response. Be prepared to label a given diagram of a reflex arc.

(50) Explain the importance of a reflex action?

(51) Explain why the dark area of the spinal cord is called the grey matter.

The nervous system

The nervous system:

- Detects changes or stimuli inside the body and from the surroundings.
- Processes the information.
- Initiates responses.

Receptors, which range from specialised sensory cells, such as those in the skin, to the more complex sense organs such as the ear and eye, detect the information from inside the body and from the surroundings.

It is the role of the central nervous system (CNS), which is made up of the brain and spinal cord, to process the information and initiate a response.

Effectors bring about responses. Effectors may be muscles or glands.

Sensory receptors detect one form of energy and convert it into electrical energy. They are acting as transducers. The electrical impulses travel along nerves and are called nerve impulses. Some nerves bring information to the CNS and others take the information away.

Reflex arc

- A reflex action is a rapid, involuntary response resulting from nervous impulses initiated by a stimulus. The action is involuntary in that the brain is not involved. Reflex actions are generally protective in function.
- The following describes a typical reflex action – the nerve pathways involved in the flexion of the arm in response to touching a hot surface:
  - Stimulus – the hot surface.
  - Receptor – temperature and pain receptors in the skin.
  - Sensory neurone sends impulse to spinal cord.
  - Relay neurone connects sensory neurone to motor neurone.
  - Motor neurone sends impulse to an effector (muscle).
  - Response – arm muscles contract and the hand is removed from surface.

The nervous pathways of a reflex arc.

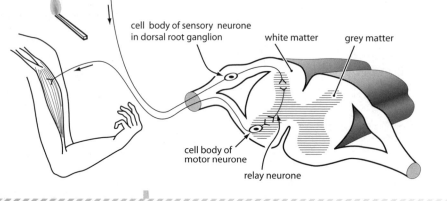

cell body of sensory neurone in dorsal root ganglion

white matter

grey matter

cell body of motor neurone

relay neurone

Although many reflexes are protective, actions such as blinking, coughing and swallowing are also co-ordinated by reflexes. With any reflex action there is also a pathway for impulses to be sent to the brain via ascending nerve fibres that originate at synapses in the grey matter of the spinal cord. The brain may store this information or it may relate the information with sense data from, say, the eyes. As a result of receiving this extra information impulses may be sent from the brain to modify the response. Sometimes the response is over-ridden by the brain along inhibitory nerve fibres.

Nerve net.

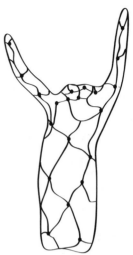

Nerve nets in hydra

The stimuli received by many sense organs, such as the eyes, are very complex and require very differing responses. For example, bright light may involve blinking whereas seeing a friend in the distance may involve walking in their direction.

Simple organisms do not possess many receptors and effectors. The sense receptors respond to a limited number of stimuli and the number of effectors is small. An example of a simple organism is the hydra, which is a member of the jellyfish group (coelenterates). The hydra does not have a recognisable brain or true muscles. It has a nervous system known as a nerve net which is a very simple system compared to mammalian nervous systems. Nerve nets connect sensory photoreceptors and touch-sensitive nerve cells located in the body wall and tentacles.

The nerve net consists of simple nerve cells with short extensions joined to each other and branching in a number of different directions. This means that the transmission of the nerve impulse is slow.

Grade boost

The simple nerve net system enables hydra to sense its surroundings and respond to stimuli in an appropriate way. Responses may be to avoid danger by retracting the body from a predator.

quickfire

(52) What is the disadvantage of a nerve net system?

Neurones

There are three types of neurones:

- Sensory – which bring impulses from the sense organs or receptors into the CNS.
- Motor – these carry impulses from the CNS to the effector organs (muscles or glands).
- Connector (intermediate or relay) – these receive impulses from sensory neurones or other intermediate neurones and relay them to motor neurones or other intermediate neurones.

Pointer

Neurones are highly specialised cells that generate and transmit electrical charges called impulses or action potentials.

Pointer

You are required to know the structure of a motor neurone only.

A mammalian motor neurone.

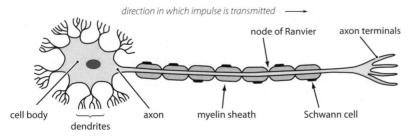

direction in which impulse is transmitted ⟶

node of Ranvier   axon terminals

cell body   axon   myelin sheath   Schwann cell

dendrites

Key terms

Key terms

Resting potential = the potential difference between the inside and the outside of a membrane when a nerve impulse is not being conducted

quickfire

㊳ Which type of neurone carries nerve impulses to an effector?

Grade boost

Axons are surrounded by Schwann cells which protect and provide insulation because their membranes are rich in a lipid called myelin.

Measurement of nerve impulse.

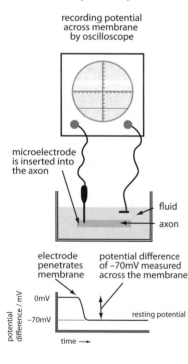

recording potential across membrane by oscilloscope

microelectrode is inserted into the axon

fluid

axon

electrode penetrates membrane

potential difference of −70mV measured across the membrane

0mV

−70mV

resting potential

potential difference / mV

time →

Each cell consists of a cell body containing a nucleus, and granular cytoplasm containing many ribosomes. These ribosomes are grouped together forming Nissl granules, which are concerned with the formation of neurotransmitter substances. Many thin extensions carry impulses towards the cell body. The short extensions are called dendrites. These receive impulses from other nerve cells and carry the information towards the cell body. Some neurones also have a long membrane-covered cytoplasmic extension, the axon, which transmits impulses from the cell body. At its end, an axon divides into branches which form synapses with other neurones.

Peripheral neurones are surrounded by and supported by Schwann cells. In some cases these grow around the axons of the nerve cells to form a multi-layered fatty myelin sheath found only in vertebrate nervous systems. This acts as an electrical insulator and speeds up the transmission of impulses. The myelin sheath has thin areas at intervals, nodes of Ranvier, which are important in impulse transmission.

The nerve impulse

The electrical charge associated with a typical nerve impulse is very small (50 millivolts). Nevertheless, nerve impulses can be recorded and measured using an apparatus which is sensitive to small electrical changes. Impulses can be picked up from the nerve through a pair of microelectrodes and fed into a cathode ray oscilloscope. This can measure the magnitude and speed of transmission of impulses and analyse the pattern of impulses generated in different parts of the nervous system.

Neurones transmit electrical impulses along the cell surface membrane surrounding the axon. Experiments involving inserting microelectrodes into axons and measuring the changes in electrical charge have shown that in a resting axon, the inside of the membrane has a negative electrical charge compared to the outside.

- **Resting potentials** are typically minus values, the minus indicating the inside is negative with respect to the outside. The membrane is said to be polarised. How does this happen?
- Sodium and potassium ions are transported across the membrane against a concentration gradient by active transport.
- This involves sodium–potassium exchange pumps (these are trans-membrane proteins) which maintain the concentration and an uneven distribution of sodium ions and potassium ions across the membrane.
- However, the Na^+ ions are passed out faster than the K^+ ions are brought in. Also K^+ ions are able to diffuse back out faster than the Na^+ ions can diffuse back in. The net result is that the outside of the membrane is positive compared to the inside.
- The outward movement of positive ions means that the inside becomes slightly negative.

The action potential

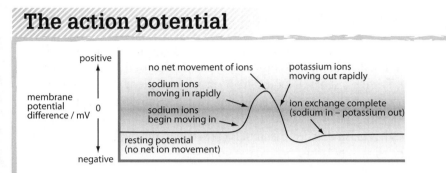

When a nerve impulse is initiated the resting potential changes:

- Nerve impulses are due to changes in the permeability of nerve cell membrane to K^+ ions and Na^+ ions which leads to changes in the potential difference across the membrane and the formation of action potential.

- Suitable stimulation of an axon results in change of potential across the membrane from a negative inside value of about $-70mV$ to a positive inside value of $+40mV$. This change is called an **action potential** and lasts about three milliseconds. The membrane is said to be **depolarised**.

- When the resting potential is re-established, the axon membrane is said to be repolarised.

- The action potential is the result of a sudden increase in the permeability of the membrane to Na^+. This allows a sudden influx of Na^+ which depolarises the membrane.

- A fraction of a second after this, depolarisation the K^+ diffuse out and repolarises the membrane. There is an overshoot of K^+ leaving as the K^+/Na^+ pump restores the ionic balance. This is called the refractory period during which another action potential cannot be generated. This time delay ensures a unidirectional impulse and limits frequency.

Ion exchange during passage of an action potential.

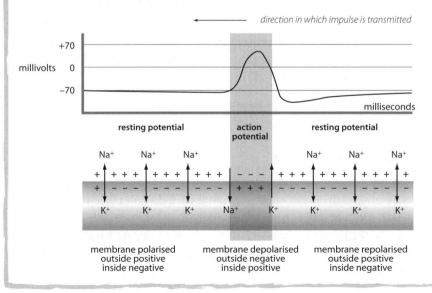

Key terms

Action potential =
a change that occurs in the electrical charge across the membrane of an axon when it is stimulated and a nerve impulse passes.

Depolarisation =
a temporary reversal of charges on the membrane of a neurone that takes place when a nerve impulse is transmitted.

Grade boost

Refer to sodium ions or potassium ions rather than merely sodium or potassium.

Pointer

Three sodium ions are passed out for every two potassium ions that are passed in.

54 Give the figure for the resting potential.

55 What is the significance of the refractory period?

Grade boost

You should state that the action potential, rather than the impulse, jumps from node to node in a myelinated nerve.

Key term

Saltatory conduction
= transmission of a nerve impulse along a myelinated axon in which the action potential jumps from one node of Ranvier to another.

≫ *Pointer*

Myelinated neurones transmit action potentials at a speed of 100 metres per second! In unmyelinated neurones the transmission speed is only one to three metres per second.

NEATH PORT TALBOT COLLEGE
LIBRARY
NEATH CAMPUS

⦿◉⫷⫷⫷ **quickfire**

56 State two factors that increase the speed of nerve impulse transmission.

⩘ Grade boost

Myelinated axons use less ATP to transmit a nerve impulse than a non-myelinated axon of the same diameter because active transport of sodium ions occurs only at the nodes rather than the whole length of the axon.

How the action potential travels along an axon

The action potential causes a small electric current across the membrane and as a portion of the membrane is depolarised, depolarisation of the next portion is initiated. There is a series of local currents propagated along the axon. The sodium pump is active all the time and behind the transmission; this pump restores the resting potential. Once the resting potential is restored, another impulse can be transmitted. As the impulse progresses, the outflux of K^+ causes the neurone to be repolarised behind the impulse.

Properties of nerves and impulses

The 'all or nothing law' – the size of the impulse is independent of the size of the stimulus.

If the intensity of a stimulus is below a certain threshold intensity, no action potential is initiated. But, if the intensity of the stimulus exceeds the threshold value, an action potential *is* initiated. Any further increase in the intensity of the stimulus does not give a greater action potential. Instead, the frequency of action potentials changes. A strong stimulus produces a greater frequency of action potentials as the intensity of stimulation increases. A weak stimulus generates fewer action potentials.

Factors affecting the speed of conduction of the nerve impulse

Two factors are important in determining the speed of conduction of the nerve impulse:

- Myelination speeds up the rate of transmission by insulating the axon. Depolarisation and action potentials cannot occur in the myelinated parts of the axon, except at the nodes of Ranvier. The result is that the impulse jumps from one node to the next, speeding the overall passage along the axon. This is called **saltatory conduction**.
- The diameter of the axon – the greater the diameter of the axon, the greater the velocity of transmission. Giant axons are found in the squid and are thought to be associated with rapid escape responses.

Synapses

Structure of a synapse

Most junctions between neurones take the form of chemical synapses. Branches of axons lie close to dendrites of other neurones but do not touch; there is a gap of about 20μm between them. When impulses are transmitted, this gap is crossed by the secretion of a neurotransmitter from the axon membrane (pre-synaptic membrane), which diffuses across the space to stimulate the dendritic membrane (postsynaptic membrane).

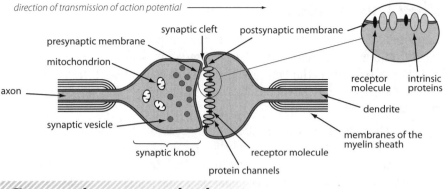

direction of transmission of action potential

synaptic cleft

presynaptic membrane

postsynaptic membrane

mitochondrion

axon

receptor molecule

intrinsic proteins

synaptic vesicle

dendrite

synaptic knob

receptor molecule

membranes of the myelin sheath

protein channels

Synaptic transmission

The arrival of the impulses at the synaptic knob alters its permeability, allowing calcium ions to enter. The influx of calcium ions causes the synaptic vesicle to fuse with the presynaptic membrane, so releasing the transmitter (acetylcholine) into the synaptic cleft. When the transmitter diffuses across the gap (synaptic cleft), it attaches to a receptor site on the postsynaptic membrane, depolarising it and so initiating an impulse in the next neurone.

The postsynaptic membrane contains specific protein receptors with which the transmitter molecules combine. Once combined, protein channels open up in the membrane, allowing sodium ions to diffuse from the cleft into the postsynaptic neurone. If the membrane becomes sufficiently depolarised, an action potential is initiated in the axon of the postsynaptic neurone.

Acetylcholine, when released, is quickly destroyed by enzymes in the synaptic cleft, so its effect is limited and the merging of impulses is prevented. If insufficient acetylcholine is released, the postsynaptic membrane will not be stimulated. The enzyme which destroys acetylcholine is called cholinesterase. The resulting choline and ethanoic acid diffuse back across the synaptic cleft to reform acetylcholine. ATP is required to re-form transmitter molecules and store them in vesicles.

Function of synapses

The function of the synapse is to convey action potentials between neurones:

- Transmit information between neurones.
- Pass impulses in one direction only.
- Act as junctions – since synaptic vesicles are present only in the knob of the presynaptic neurone, impulses can only pass across a synapse in one direction.
- Filter out low level stimuli. That is, remove 'background noise' from the nervous system.
- To protect the response system from overstimulation.

>> *Pointer*

Neurones are not in direct contact with each other but are separated by tiny gaps known as synapses. The main role of the synapse is to convey action potentials between neurones.

<<<<< quicKFire

57 Explain why mitochondria are found abundantly in the presynaptic region.

<<<<< quicKFire

58 Name the type of movement of sodium ions across the membrane.

Grade boost

Devise a flowchart to help describe synaptic transmission.

<<<<< quicKFire

59 Explain why there is a continuous supply of acetylcholine.

Key terms

Neuromuscular junction = a synapse that occurs between a neurone and a muscle.

Photoperiod = a period of illumination.

>> *Pointer*

The topic of synapses brings together several other topics already encountered, such as, membranes, diffusion, enzyme action, mitochondria.

>> *Pointer*

You are not required to study psychoactive drugs in any detail.

Grade boost

Caffeine increases the metabolic rate in presynaptic cells. That is, there is increased production of ATP which stimulates neurotransmitter synthesis.

Effect of drugs

Amplification at the synapse may be due to chemicals mimicking the action of natural transmitters. That is, they have the same shape and affect the postsynaptic neurone in the same way that the transmitter would. They may prevent the breakdown of the transmitter, for example, by inhibiting the enzyme that normally does this.

A psychoactive drug is a chemical substance that acts primarily on the central nervous system where it alters brain function resulting in temporary changes in perception, mood, consciousness and behaviour. Most of these drugs were originally developed to be used therapeutically as medication. Examples of psychoactive drugs include tobacco, cannabis, amphetamines, ecstasy, cocaine and heroin.

Most drugs that affect the nervous system influence the transmission of nerve impulses across synapses. These drugs can be classified into two types:

- Excitory drugs, which stimulate the nervous system by creating more action potentials in postsynaptic membranes.
- Inhibitory drugs, which inhibit the nervous system by creating fewer action potentials in postsynaptic membranes.

Organophosphorous insecticides block the enzyme that breaks down the transmitter substance once they are attached to the receptor proteins of the postsynaptic membrane. This prolongs the effect of the neurotransmitters. Without cholinesterase acting as a cholinesterase inhibitor, acetylcholine remains in the synaptic cleft and causes repeated firing of the postsynaptic neurone. If the inhibitor is acting at a **neuromuscular junction**, repeated contractions of the muscle occur. That is, the nervous system becomes overactive and muscles contract uncontrollably.

Photoperiodism

Plant responses are slow because co-ordination is achieved by chemicals, similar to hormones in animals. Plants do not have a nervous system, instead growth is co-ordinated by plant growth substances. One response to light in plants is called **photoperiodism**. This is the response of a plant to relative lengths of daylight and darkness. Flowering is influenced by day length.

Phytochrome

The photoreceptor responsible for absorbing light has been identified as phytochrome, a blue-green pigment found in very minute quantities in plants. Phytochrome exists in two forms that are interconvertible:

$$\text{phytochrome 660 (Pr)} \underset{\text{far-red light}}{\overset{\text{red light}}{\rightleftharpoons}} \text{phytochrome 730 (Pfr)}$$

On absorbing light of a particular wavelength, each form of phytochrome is converted to the other form.

Pfr is unstable and, during the hours of darkness, slowly reverts back to Pr, which accumulates.

The plant measures day length or length of darkness by the amount of phytochrome existing in each of the two forms and in daylight Pfr is the main form.

The photoperiodic stimulus is detected by the leaves of a plant. This can be demonstrated using a single plant and exposing one leaf to light whilst covering up the remainder of the leaves. The stimulus must be transmitted through the plant to the buds, which then develop flowers. Flowering in plants is thought to be initiated by the hormone 'florigen'.

Photoperiodism

Photoperiodism is the term used to describe the influence of relative periods of light and darkness on flowering. Flowering plants can be divided into three groups according to their photoperiodic requirements prior to the production of flowers:

- Day neutral plants – flowering does not seem to be affected by the day length, e.g. tomato, cotton, cucumber.

- Long-day plants – flowering is induced by exposure to dark periods (number of hours) shorter than a critical length, e.g. cabbage, petunia.

- Short-day plants – flowering is induced by exposure to dark periods longer than a critical length, e.g. chrysanthemum, tobacco, poinsettia.

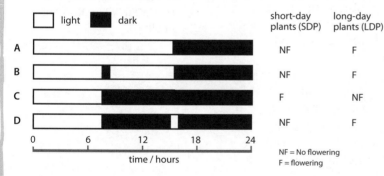

In short-day plants flowering is inhibited by exposure to red light, and exposure to far-red light will bring about flowering. It seems that these plants will flower only if the level of Pfr is low enough, but the situation in the long-day plants is reversed and flowering is triggered by high levels of Pfr. The length of the photoperiod is less critical than the length of the dark period and if the photoperiod is interrupted with a short period of darkness, flowering still follows.

If the dark period is interrupted by as little as one minute's exposure to light, flowering is prevented. Red light is most effective in this respect yet the effect of red light treatment can be overcome if the plant is immediately exposed to infrared light.

Grade boost

Sunlight contains more light of wavelength 660 nm (red light) than 730 nm; therefore during daylight Pr is converted to Pfr, which accumulates.

quickfire

60 What is the name of the hormone which initiates flowering and in which part of the plant is it found?

⟫ Pointer

Historically, plants are categorised as short-day or long-day. This is unfortunate as it is the length of the dark period that is crucial.

quickfire

61 Look at the figure and in each case explain why flowering takes place in short-day or long-day plants.

quickfire

62 What are the practical applications for horticulturalists of knowing when plants flower?

Summary: Metabolism, Microbiology and Homeostasis

Respiration

- A series of reactions taking place in cells resulting in the release of energy in the form of ATP from organic compounds such as glucose.
- ATP is made from ADP and inorganic phosphate by phosphorylation.
- The breakdown of glucose involves four stages: glycolysis, the link reaction, Krebs cycle and the electron transport chain.
- Glycolysis takes place in the cytoplasm of the cell and involves the splitting of glucose to pyruvate with the release of ATP and reduced NAD.
- The link reaction involves the conversion of pyruvate to acetyl CoA which enters the mitochondrion to join the Krebs cycle.
- The Krebs cycle results in the formation of reduced carriers, ATP and carbon dioxide.
- The electron transport chain uses the energy of electrons to pump protons with the formation of ATP by ATP synthetase.
- The production of ATP in the electron transport system of by aerobic repiration is called oxidative phosphorylation.
- Aerobic respiration has the potential to produce 38 molecules of ATP per molecule of glucose, whereas anaerobic respiration involves only glycolysis and produces 2 molecules of ATP.

Photosynthesis

- Photosynthesis takes place in the chloroplast and uses light energy to synthesise organic molecules from carbon dioxide and water.
- Photosynthetic pigments are grouped together to form antenna complexes which funnel photons of light to one of two reaction centres, PSI and PSII.
- The absorption of light energy boosts the electrons within the reaction centre to a higher energy level.
- The electrons are passed through a series of carriers to form ATP by photophosphorylation.
- This light-dependent stage takes place in the thylakoid membrane of the chloroplast and produces ATP and NADPH.
- The synthesis of ATP occurs by cyclic and non-cyclic photophosphorylation.
- The photolysis of water provides electrons to replace those lost from the reaction centre.
- The light-independent stage takes place in the stroma of the chloroplast and involves the fixation of carbon dioxide using the products of the light-independent stage, ATP and NADPH, to convert it to carbohydrate.

Microbiology

- Bacteria can be classified according to their shape and the Gram stain technique.
- Bacteria reproduce quickly under optimum conditions of nutrients, temperature and pH.
- Bacteria are cultured using sterile techniques.
- Bacteria may be counted using viable counts or total counts.
- Samples need to be diluted by serial dilution to produce results that are countable.
- An important use of large-scale industrial fermentation is the production of penicillin using the fungus, *Penicillium* sp. Penicillin is produced by batch fermentation and is a secondary metabolite produced when nutrients are depleted.

Populations

- The numbers of individuals in a population are increased by births and immigration and decreased by deaths and emigration.
- The size of a population is determined by environmental resistance and the carrying capacity.
- Population changes may be density-dependent or density-independent.
- Population shows a pattern of growth and follows an S-shaped curve.
- Pests may be controlled by chemical and biological methods, each method has its relative advantages and disadvantages.
- Decomposers are the organisms involved in the cycling of nutrients in ecosystems.
- Several different species of bacteria play an important role in the cycling of nitrogen.

Homeostasis

- Homeostasis is the maintenance of a constant internal environment, relying on negative feedback to produce an opposing change.
- Excretion is the removal of metabolic waste products from the body.
- Fish, birds, insects and mammals produce different excretory products.
- The kidneys are the main organs of the urinary system and are made up of numerous nephrons.
- Small molecules pass from the blood by ultra filtration and useful substances are reabsorbed into the blood as the filtrate passes along the nephron.
- Osmoregulators in the hypothalamus monitor the water potential of the blood, and the reabsorption of water is controlled by the secretion of ADH from the pituitary gland.

Nervous system

- The nervous system controls and co-ordinates actions by detecting stimuli using receptors, and processes the information and initiates responses by effectors.
- A basic reflex arc involves receptors, sensory, relay and motor neurones, effectors.
- Nerve transmission involves changes in permeability of the axon membrane to sodium ions resulting in the production of an action potential.
- The speed of transmission of an impulse is affected by the presence of a myelin sheath and the axon diameter.
- The transfer of information from one neuron to the next involves the secretion of a neurotransmitter across synapses.
- Synaptic transmission is affected by drugs.

Photoperiodism

- Plant responses are slower than animals as they involve only hormones.
- Photoperiodism is the response of a plant to the relative length of daylight and darkness.
- Photoperiodism involves a light-sensitive pigment, phytochrome, which exists in two forms and the plant measures day length by the relative amount of phytochrome existing in each of the two forms.

Knowledge and Understanding

BY5 Environment, Genetics and Evolution

This unit looks at the way in which characteristics are passed from one generation to the next and how this can produce genetic variation within a population. Populations may be isolated and, in time, the genes within each population may alter, leading to the formation of new species. Information is passed from one generation to the next through sexual reproduction and the production of gametes by the process of meiosis.

DNA acts as a store of genetic information which must be replicated in each generation. DNA also acts as a template which determines the characteristics of an organism through protein synthesis. Changes in DNA may occur through mutation and this contributes to variation. The environment also contributes to genetic variation. A significant scientific advance in recent years has been the development of technology that allows genes to be manipulated, altered and transferred from organism to organism.

Ecosystems are maintained by light energy from the sun that plants convert by photosynthesis into carbohydrate. This in turn is consumed by all organisms to release energy for their survival. The unit looks at how energy flows through the ecosystem. It also covers the conflict between human needs and the conservation of natural resources.

Revision checklist

Tick column 1 when you have completed brief revision notes.
Tick column 2 when you think you have a good grasp of the topic.
Tick column 3 during final revision when you feel you have mastery of the topic.

		1	2	3	Notes
p54	**The genetic code and cell function**				
p54	Replication				
p55	The genetic code				
p56	Protein synthesis				
p59	Meiosis				
p62	**Human reproduction**				
p62	Male reproductive system				
p62	Female reproductive system				
p63	Gametogenesis				
p66	Pregnancy testing				
p67	**Sexual reproduction in plants**				
p67	Structure of an insect-pollinated flower				
p67	Pollination				
p70	Fertilisation				
p71	Structure of the seed				

Key term

Template = a blueprint from which a copy is made.

≫ *Pointer*

Consider reviewing DNA structure from BY1.

≫ *Pointer*

DNA replication uses complementary base pairings to produce identical copies.

◉ **quickfire**

① Explain the effect of adding an inhibitor of DNA polymerase to a cell.

◉ **quickfire**

② In this experiment, why were the bacteria which had incorporated the heavy isotope of nitrogen washed before transfer to a medium containing normal nitrogen?

≫ *Pointer*

Bacteria will incorporate nitrogen from their growing medium into any new DNA they produce.

▲ **Grade boost**

The experiments involved the use of an ultra-centrifuge. This rotates centrifuge tubes containing liquid suspensions at very high speeds, which results in the denser particles separating out at a lower point in the tube than the lighter particles.

The genetic code and cell function

DNA has two major functions in the cell:

- Replication, in dividing cells.
- Carrying information for protein synthesis in all cells.

Replication

Chromosomes must make copies of themselves so that when cells divide, each daughter cell must receive an exact copy of the genetic information. This copying of DNA is called replication and takes place in a cell during interphase. Replication occurs as follows:

- The hydrogen bonds holding the base pairs together break and the two halves of the molecule separate.
- DNA unwinds and as the strands separate, the enzyme DNA polymerase catalyses the addition of free nucleotides to the exposed bases.
- Each chain acts as a **template** so that free nucleotides can be joined to their complementary bases by DNA polymerase.
- The result is two DNA molecules, each made up of one newly synthesised chain and one chain conserved from the original molecule.
- This is called the semi-conservative hypothesis.

Experiments were carried out to confirm the hypothesis:

1. The scientists cultured the bacterium, *Escherichia coli*, for several generations on a medium containing amino acids made with the heavy isotope of nitrogen ^{15}N. The bacteria incorporated the ^{15}N into their nucleotides and then into their DNA so that all the DNA contained ^{15}N. They extracted the bacterial DNA and centrifuged it. The DNA settled at a low point in the tube.

2. The ^{15}N bacteria were washed, then transferred to a medium containing the normal, lighter form of nitrogen, ^{14}N, and were allowed to divide once more.

3. When extracts of DNA from this first generation culture were centrifuged, it was shown to have a mid-point density, since half the strand was made up of the original strand of ^{15}N DNA and the other half was made up of the new strand containing ^{14}N.

4. When extracts were taken from the second generation grown in ^{14}N, the DNA settled at mid points and high points in the tube. This was conclusive evidence for the semi-conservative hypothesis.

Semi-conservative hypothesis.

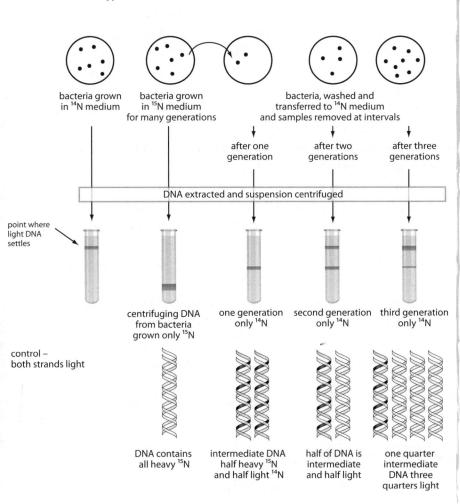

point where light DNA settles

control – both strands light

Key term

Gene = length of DNA on a chromosome normally coding for a particular polypeptide.

③ Why is the process of DNA replication described as semi-conservative?

≫ Pointer

The semi-conservative theory was proposed by Watson and Crick in 1954 and confirmed shortly after by the evidence provided by Meselson and Stahl's experiments.

quickfire

④ If the bases of the original strand of DNA are GCATTAGC, what would be the equivalent sequence of bases on the newly formed strand?

Grade boost

Using coloured pens draw a diagram to show how two complementary strands of DNA unwind into separate strands. Starting with the parent strands, carry out the process for three generations.

The genetic code

DNA acts as a store of genetic information. Chromosomes are divided up into thousands of shorter sections called **genes**. This information is called the genetic code. The codes carried by DNA determine what reactions can take place in an organism. Genes control the formation of enzymes which are proteins. By determining which enzymes are produced, the DNA can determine the characteristics of an organism.

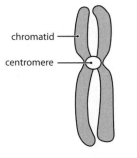

chromatid

centromere

Structure of a chromosome.

Grade boost

DNA is the starting point for protein synthesis since the sequence of bases on DNA, the genetic code, determines the primary structure of a protein. It is the sequence by which various amino acids are joined together to form a particular polypeptide chain.

⑤ How many bases are required to code for a chain of eight consecutive amino acids?

⑥ Explain how a change in one base along the DNA may result in a protein becoming non-functional.

≫ Pointer

Consider reviewing previous work from BY1 regarding the three different types of RNA: messenger RNA, ribosomal RNA and transfer RNA.

Grade boost

DNA does not leave the nucleus but acts as a template for the production of mRNA, which carries the instructions needed for protein synthesis from the nucleus to the cytoplasm. The function of the ribosomes situated in the cytoplasm is to provide a suitable surface for the attachment of mRNA and the assembly of protein.

Why is the code a triplet code?

- Each amino acid must have its own code of bases on the DNA.
- There are four different bases in DNA (adenine, guanine, cytosine and thymine) but there are over twenty different amino acids.
- If one base coded for one amino acid it would be possible to make only four amino acids.
- If two bases coded for one amino acid it would be possible to produce 16 different codes to make 16 amino acids.
- Having three bases for each amino acid would give a permutation of 64 codes, more than enough to make 20 amino acids.
- As the code has three bases it is called the triplet code.
- Amino acids are in fact coded by more than one DNA base triplet. Also there are some codes that do not code for amino acids at all! These have been called 'stop' and 'start' codes.
- It is the sequence of bases in the DNA chain that codes for the sequence of amino acids in a polypeptide.
- The portion of DNA which codes for a whole polypeptide is called a gene. (This is the basis of the one gene – one polypeptide hypothesis.)
- Each amino acid is coded for by three bases (the triplet code) called a codon.
- All the codons are universal, that is, they are exactly the same for all living organisms.
- The code is non-overlapping in that each triplet is read separately.

Protein synthesis

The basic process of protein synthesis occurs as follows:

- DNA acts as a template providing the instructions in the form of a long sequence of nucleotides.
- A complementary section of part of this sequence is made into mRNA by a process called transcription.
- The mRNA acts as a template to which complementary tRNA molecules attach and the amino acids they carry are linked to form a polypeptide by a process called translation.

Transcription

- The enzyme DNA helicase acts on a specific region of the DNA molecule, called the cistron, to break the hydrogen bonds between the bases, causing the two strands to separate and expose the nucleotide bases in that region.

- The enzyme RNA polymerase links to the template strand of DNA at the beginning of the sequence to be copied. The double-stranded DNA first unwinds and then unzips in the relevant region.

- Transcription occurs when free RNA nucleotides align themselves opposite the template strand.

- Because of the complementary relationship between the bases in DNA and the free nucleotides, cytosine in the DNA attracts a guanine, guanine a cytosine, thymine an adenine, and adenine a uracil.

- RNA polymerase moves along the DNA forming bonds that add nucleotides one at a time to the RNA. This results in the synthesis of a molecule of mRNA alongside the unzipped portion of DNA. Behind the RNA polymerase the DNA strands rejoin to reform the double helix.

- Each amino acid was coded for by a DNA codon. The mRNA molecule carries complementary RNA codons.

- The mRNA carries the DNA code out of the nucleus through a nuclear pore to the cytoplasm and attaches itself to a ribosome consisting of ribosomal RNA and protein.

Transcription.

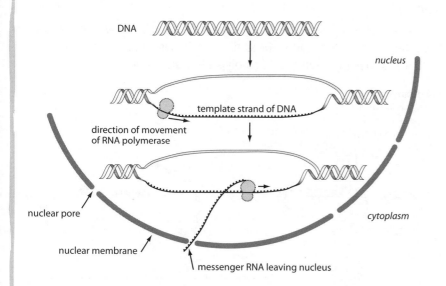

Pointer

In RNA there is no thymine. It is replaced by uracil which pairs with adenine.

quickfire

⑦ A sequence of bases along the template strand of DNA is CCAGGAGAGA ATTCATTT. What is the sequence of bases on the mRNA molecule that has been transcribed from this part of the DNA molecule? How many amino acids does the sequence code for?

Grade boost

Sometimes the primary structure of a polypeptide chain acts as a functional protein but usually the polypeptide needs to be converted to secondary, tertiary or quaternary structures. Consider reviewing your BY1 notes on 'Levels of protein structure' and the involvement of the Golgi body.

Pointer

It is highly likely that the exam paper will contain a question on protein synthesis. Be prepared to describe a specific part of the process, to decode base sequences or to write an essay on the complete process.

>> Pointer

Amino acids are carried to the ribosomes by transfer RNA molecules (tRNA). Each tRNA carries its own specific amino acid at the amino acid attachment site. The specific amino acid is determined by the triplet of bases referred to as the anticodon.

Grade boost

The ribosome acts as a framework moving along the mRNA, reading the code, holding the codon–anticodon complex together until two amino acids join. The ribosome moves along adding one amino acid at a time until the polypeptide chain is assembled.

⑧ A codon on a section of mRNA has the sequence of bases AUC. List the sequence of bases found on the template strand of DNA that formed the mRNA codon and the tRNA anticodon that attaches to this codon.

⑨ Name the molecule that:
(a) moves through the nuclear pore to the cytoplasm.
(b) carries an amino acid to the ribosome.
(c) is transcribed but not translated.

Translation

Each ribosome is made up of two sub-units, with a smaller sub-unit having two sites for the attachment of tRNA molecules. This means that two tRNA molecules are associated with a ribosome at any one time.

The process of translation happens as follows:

- A ribosome becomes attached to the starting codon (AUG) at one end of the mRNA molecule.

- The first tRNA with the anticodon complementary to the first codon on the mRNA attaches itself to the ribosome. Then a second tRNA with an anticodon complementary to the second codon on the mRNA attaches to the other attachment site. The two amino acids are sufficiently close for a peptide bond to form between them. The first tRNA leaves the ribosome, leaving an attachment site vacant. The ribosome now moves one codon along the mRNA strand.

- One site binds tRNA with the growing polypeptide; the other site is for tRNA carrying the next amino acid in the sequence.

- Translation by ribosomes allows the assembly of amino acids into polypeptides according to the original DNA code. A ribosomal enzyme catalyses peptide bond formation between an amino acid on one tRNA and the growing polypeptide on the other tRNA.

- A ribosome passes along mRNA, one codon at a time, the tRNA with the appropriate anticodon fills the vacant slot and the amino acid forms a peptide bond with the last member of the chain until a stop codon is reached.

- Each time one ribosome moves along the mRNA a molecule of polypeptide is produced.

- Usually a number of ribosomes can be found on a single mRNA each reading from the coded information at the same time. This is called a polysome system and so many molecules of a polypeptide are formed.

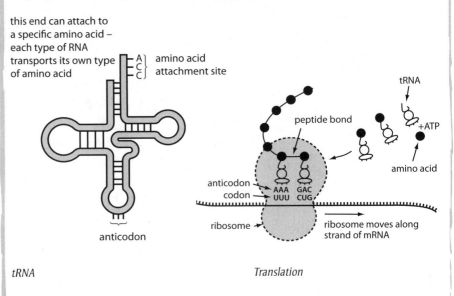

tRNA   *Translation*

Amino acid activation

Once the tRNA is released from its specific amino acid, it is free to collect another amino acid from the amino acid pool in the cell. Energy from ATP is required for the specific amino acid to attach itself to the tRNA. This process is referred to as activation.

Key term

Homologous = a pair of chromosomes, one maternal and one paternal, that have the same gene loci and therefore determine the same features.

Meiosis

The diagram shows that meiosis involves two divisions of the cell.

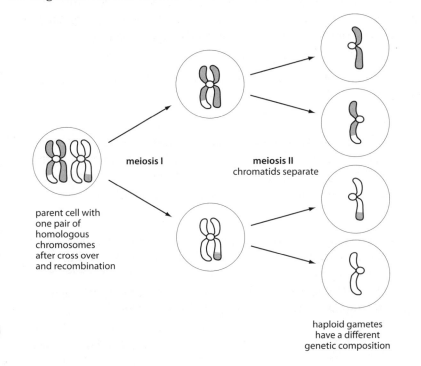

parent cell with one pair of homologous chromosomes after cross over and recombination

meiosis I

meiosis II
chromatids separate

haploid gametes
have a different
genetic composition

Grade boost

Meiosis takes place in the reproductive organs of both plants and animals. It results in the formation of haploid gametes. In contrast to mitosis, meiosis produces cells that are not genetically identical. In fact, meiosis plays an important role in bringing about genetic variation in living organisms.

Summary of meiosis

Meiosis I – **homologous** chromosomes pair up and their chromatids wrap around each other and equivalent portions of these chromatids may be exchanged in a process called crossing over. By the end of this stage the homologous pair separate with one chromosome of each pair going into one of the two daughter cells. This results in two daughter nuclei containing half the number of chromosomes of the parent nucleus.

Meiosis II – where the chromatids move apart and the two new haploid nuclei divide again in a division identical to that of mitosis. The net result is that four haploid nuclei are formed from the parent nucleus each containing half the number of chromosomes.

When the cell is not dividing it is said to be in interphase. During this phase the DNA content of the cell is doubled and new cell organelles are also formed.

≫ Pointer

The names of the subdivisions of prophase I are not required.

quickfire

⑩ What is the main difference between prophase of mitosis and prophase I of meiosis?

quickfire

⑪ What is a chromatid?

≫ Pointer

Be prepared to identify stages in given diagrams in the exam. In particular, distinguish between stages in meiosis I and II.

Grade boost

In a homologous pair both alleles may be dominant, or one recessive and the other dominant, or both may be recessive. It is the different forms of the same alleles that are exchanged during crossing over.

quickfire

⑫ State the two ways in which meiosis leads to an increase in genetic variety.

Grade boost

Prepare cards showing diagrams of the stages of meiosis and name the stages on the back of the cards. Practise placing the cards in the correct order.

Meiosis I

Prophase I

The chromosomes become shorter and thicker and split into two chromatids. In cells where centrioles are present, i.e. animals and lower plants, the centrioles move to the poles of the cells and microtubules begin to radiate from them forming asters. This results in the formation of the spindle.

This stage differs from that of mitosis as homologous chromosomes associate in pairs and each pair is called a bivalent. Each bivalent consists of four strands, made up of two chromosomes, each splits into two chromatids. These chromatids wrap around each other and then partially repel each other but remain joined at certain points called chiasmata. At these points chromatids may break and recombine with a different but equivalent chromatid.

This exchange of pieces of chromosomes is called crossing over.

At the end of prophase the nuclear membrane disintegrates and the nucleolus disappears.

Metaphase 1

At this stage, when the pairs of homologous chromosomes align themselves on the equator of the spindle, the maternal and paternal chromosomes are arranged randomly. This random distribution and consequent independent assortment of chromosomes produces new genetic combinations.

Anaphase 1

The chromosomes in each bivalent separate and one of each pair is pulled to one pole, its sister chromosome to the opposite pole. Thus each pole receives only one of each homologous pair of chromosomes and because of their random arrangement at metaphase these will be a random mixture of maternal and paternal chromosomes. This is called independent assortment of chromosomes and produces new genetic combinations. The chromosomes reach the opposite poles and the nuclear envelope reforms around each group of haploid chromosomes.

Telophase 1

Usually the chromosomes stay in their condensed form and meiosis II follows on immediately. In animal cells cytokinesis occurs, that is, the division of the cytoplasm to give two haploid cells. Many plant cells go straight into meiosis II with no re-formation of the spindle.

Meiosis II

Prophase II

The new spindle develops at right angles to the old spindle.

Metaphase II

The chromosomes line up separately on the equator of the spindle, with each chromosome attached to a spindle fibre by its centromere.

Anaphase II

The centromeres divide and the chromatids are pulled to opposite poles.

Telophase II

On reaching the poles the chromatids lengthen and are indistinct. The spindle disappears and the nuclear membrane re-forms. Cytokinesis takes place.

The result of these two meiotic divisions is that there are four haploid daughter cells and the genetic make-up of each cell is different.

The significance of meiosis

Meiosis is the reduction division that occurs during gamete formation in sexually reproducing organisms. In this division the diploid number of chromosomes ($2n$) is reduced to the haploid (n). Thus, when two gametes join together at fertilisation, the zygote that is formed has two complete sets of chromosomes returning to the diploid condition. However, meiosis does more than halve the number of chromosomes into a cell, it also introduces genetic variation into the gametes and therefore the zygotes that are produced. The two events that take place during meiosis that help to produce genetic variation are:

- Independent assortment of the homologous chromosomes.
- Crossing over, which happens between the chromatids of homologous chromosomes.

When these genetically different gametes fuse, randomly, at fertilisation, more variation is produced amongst the offspring.

In the long term, if a species is to survive in a constantly changing environment and to colonise new environments, sources of variation are essential. There are three ways of creating variety:

- Each of the chromosomes making up a homologous pair carries different genetic material. During sexual reproduction the **genotype** of one parent is mixed with that of the other when haploid gametes fuse.
- The different pairs of homologous chromosomes arrange themselves on the spindle during metaphase 1 of meiosis. When they subsequently separate, they do so entirely independently of each other, so that the daughter cells contain different combinations of maternal and paternal chromosomes.
- Crossing over during chiasmata formation occurs during prophase 1 of meiosis. Equivalent parts of homologous chromosomes may be exchanged, thus producing new combinations and the separation of linked genes. This process is called recombination.

Key term

Genotype = the genetic make-up of an organism.

⑬ What is the difference in the number of daughter cells formed at the end of meiosis compared with mitosis?

⑭ A horse's cells contain 64 chromosomes and those of a donkey 62 chromosomes. A mule is a cross between a horse and a donkey.
(a) How many chromosomes in the cells of a mule?
(b) From your knowledge of meiosis, suggest why mules cannot produce gametes and are therefore sterile.

》 Pointer

The sources of variation are central to the concept of evolution.

⑮ Distinguish between the terms haploid and diploid.

chromatids of homologous chromosomes twist around one another, crossing over many times

simplified represenation of a single cross over

point of breakage

result of a single cross over showing equivalent portions of the chromatid having been exchanged

Crossing over.

Pointer

>> **Pointer**

Be prepared to label given diagrams of the male and female reproductive systems and to describe the functions of the structures.

quickfire

(16) Name the structures which produce spermatozoa.

quickfire

(17) Name two structures which produce secretions that aid sperm mobility.

Human reproduction

Male reproductive system

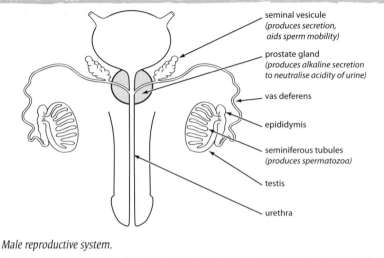

seminal vesicle (*produces secretion, aids sperm mobility*)

prostate gland (*produces alkaline secretion to neutralise acidity of urine*)

vas deferens

epididymis

seminiferous tubules (*produces spermatozoa*)

testis

urethra

Male reproductive system.

Female reproductive system

There are two ovaries each of which produces ova or eggs. They are produced in the germinal epithelium where they develop into follicles. Mature follicles migrate back to the surface when their development is complete so that the ova can be shed.

Ova are passed to the fallopian tube (oviduct) which conveys them to the uterus (womb). The uterus has muscular walls and is lined internally by a mucus membrane called the endometrium. It is well supplied with blood and is part of the womb into which the embryo implants during pregnancy and which is shed during menstruation. The uterus opens into the vagina through a ring of muscle, the cervix.

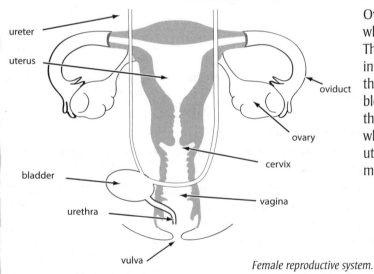

ureter

uterus

oviduct

ovary

cervix

bladder

urethra

vagina

vulva

Female reproductive system.

Gametogenesis

The production of gametes in the gonads is known as gametogenesis.

- Spermatogenesis is the formation of sperm in the testis.
- Oogenesis is the formation of eggs or ova in the ovary.

The cells of the germinal epithelium of both the testis and the ovary undergo a sequence of mitotic and meiotic divisions to form haploid gametes. It is important that the gametes are haploid so that at fertilisation the diploid number is restored.

≫ Pointer

Ensure that you know the points at which mitosis and meiosis take place in gametogenesis.

Spermatogenesis

This is the process by which spermatozoa are produced. This takes place in the germinal epithelium of the seminiferous tubule:

- The diploid spermatogonia divide many times by mitosis to produce primary spermatocytes.
- These then undergo meiosis and after the first meiotic division form haploid secondary spermatocytes.
- After the second meiotic division they form spermatids which differentiate into mature spermatozoa.

In the wall of the seminiferous tubule are the Sertoli cells. They secrete a fluid which nourishes the spermatids and protects them from the immune system of the male.

There are also groups of interstitial cells which secrete the male sex hormone.

Spermatogenesis.

Grade boost

Learn the names of the different cells in spermatogenesis.

⊙◀◀◀ quickfire

⑱ Why is the middle piece of the sperm packed with mitochondria?

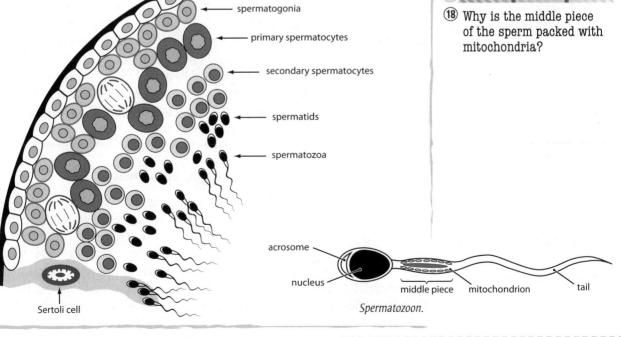

Spermatozoon.

19 State the function of:
(a) the Sertoli cells.
(b) interstitial cells.

Grade boost

Learn the names of the different cells in oogenesis.

Grade boost

About two million primary oocytes are formed in the ovary of the foetus but only about 450 will later develop into secondary oocytes after the onset of puberty.

Grade boost

Recent experiments with mice suggest that oogonia may continue to be produced after birth. If this is true for humans, this has important implications for the treatment of sub-fertility.

Oogenesis

This is the process by which ova are produced in the ovary.

- Oogonia, which are formed before birth, undergo mitosis to form primary oocytes.
- The primary oocytes start to divide by meiosis but the process stops at prophase I.
- The germinal epithelium also divides to form follicle cells which surround the primary oocytes to form primary follicles.
- The primary oocytes do not mature until just before ovulation.
- At puberty, hormones stimulate the follicles to develop further. Each month several follicles start to develop but only one matures into a fully developed Graafian follicle.
- First the primary oocyte completes the first meiotic division to form the haploid secondary oocyte and a small polar body.
- The mature Graafian follicle migrates to the surface of the ovary where it bursts and the secondary oocyte is released, a process called ovulation.
- The secondary oocyte begins the secondary meiotic division but this is arrested at metaphase unless fertilisation takes place. On fertilisation this division is completed to form a large ovum and a second polar body. Once this division has taken place the nucleus of the ovum fuses with that of the sperm to form a zygote, which will then develop into an embryo.

Sexual intercourse

So that fertilisation can take place the sperm travels in fluid called semen, from the seminiferous tubules to the oviduct of the female. Secretions from the seminal vesicles, Cowper's glands and the prostate gland, are added to the sperm to form semen. During sexual intercourse the penis is inserted into the vagina. Movements of the penis result in the ejaculation of semen into the vagina. The force of ejaculation is sufficient to propel some sperm through the cervix into the uterus, with the remainder being deposited at the top of the vagina. The sperm swim through the uterus into the oviducts by the lashing movements of their tails. However, only a small number of sperm reach the site of fertilisation in the oviduct and surround the ovum.

20 Describe what is meant by the term 'fertilisation'.

quickfire

21 Name the product of fertilisation.

Fertilisation and the acrosome reaction

Internal fertilisation ensures that the sperm are deposited in the female's reproductive tract. From here the sperm use their tails to swim through the cervix and up through the uterus to the oviduct. The sperm can remain viable for 48 hours. If ovulation has recently taken place, there will be a secondary oocyte in the oviduct. (The egg or ovum released from the Graafian follicle of the ovary dies within 24 hours unless fertilised.) The secondary oocyte is surrounded by the follicle cells and a clear membrane called the zona pellucida. Several hundred sperm surround the secondary oocyte but only one will penetrate it.

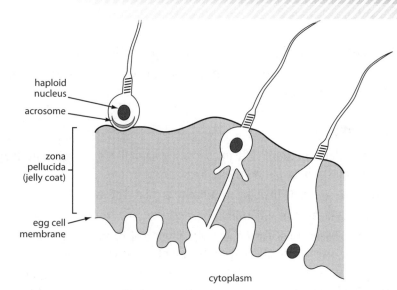

haploid nucleus

acrosome

zona pellucida (jelly coat)

egg cell membrane

cytoplasm

Acrosome reaction.

Sperm can remain viable for 12 to 24 hours after release into the female tract but can fertilise an ovum only after a process called capacitation has taken place. This process takes several hours. It involves changes in the membrane covering the acrosome, a thin cap over the nucleus of the sperm.

When the sperm reach an oocyte, contact with the zona pellucida results in the acrosome membrane rupturing and protease enzymes are released. The enzymes soften the layers of cells surrounding the oocyte. Inversion of the acrosome results in a fine needle-like filament developing at the tip of the sperm and this pierces the already softened portion of the membrane. The whole process is called the acrosome reaction and it enables the sperm to penetrate the egg. This entry stimulates reactions of the oocyte that brings about the formation of the fertilisation membrane preventing the entry of further sperm. Entry of the sperm also stimulates the completion of the second meiotic division of the oocyte nucleus. The nuclei of the ovum and sperm are drawn together and fuse to form a diploid nucleus.

Implantation

After fertilisation, the ovum or zygote begins to divide by mitosis until a hollow ball of cells, the blastocyst, is produced. The development of the zygote continues during its passage down the fallopian tube. After about three days the blastocyst reaches the uterus and embeds in the endometrium. This is called implantation.

The outer layer of the blastocyst is called the trophoblast. This layer develops into two membranes, the amnion and chorion, the latter of which grows a number of finger-like processes called chorionic villi. The villi increase the surface area for the absorption of nutrients from the wall of the uterus. The chorion also secretes a hormone called human chorionic gonadotrophin (hCG) which prevents the degeneration of the corpus luteum. (This is a structure which develops from the Graafian follicle after the ovum has been released and is important in hormone production during the early stages of pregnancy.)

quickfire

㉒ State why internal fertilisation is a necessary adaptation for life on land.

Grade boost

Consider comparing the transfer of the male nucleus to the ovum with the equivalent process in plant reproduction encountered on page 70.

quickfire

㉓ What is the function of the enzymes released after the rupture of the acrosome membrane?

quickfire

㉔ What is the function of the fertilisation membrane?

Pointer

You are not required to describe the development of the zygote further than the blastocyst stage. The description here is included only to introduce the hormone hCG. (See pregnancy testing kits on page 66.)

Detection of hCG in the urine is the basis of most pregnancy tests.

The chorionic villi eventually form part of the placenta which is attached to the foetus by the umbilical cord.

≫ Pointer

In the UK, one in six couples trying for a baby, seek medical help because of difficulty in conceiving.

Sub-fertility

- Sub-fertility is defined as difficulty in conceiving naturally for reasons affecting the male, female or both partners.
- Infertility is the complete inability to conceive a child. This is very rare.

There are two main causes of infertility:

- The failure to ovulate, usually associated with absence of, or an irregular menstrual cycle – 95% of cases are treatable with the use of a drug called clomiphene.
- A blockage of the fallopian tubes. This prevents the passage of the ovum to the site of fertilisation in the fallopian tubes. A blockage may be caused by infection and treatment usually involves microsurgery.

Pregnancy testing

Most pregnancy testing kits use monoclonal antibodies to test for the presence of the hormone, hCG in urine. A monoclonal antibody is one that responds to only one foreign antigen. The monoclonal antibody used in the kits is specific to the hormone, hCG.

Pregnancy testing kits involve the detection of hCG produced by the placenta during the early stages of pregnancy. The hormone is excreted in the urine and high levels act as a confirmation of pregnancy.

The test relies on the reaction between antibodies bound to coloured latex beads and hCG. It causes the hCG molecules to bind together and produce a colour change.

quickfire

㉕ Why is the urine used to test for pregnancy?

quickfire

㉖ Identify one antigen shown in the diagram.

quickfire

㉗ When a sample of urine from a pregnant woman is tested, a blue band appears in the large window. Using the information in the diagram explain why the blue band develops.

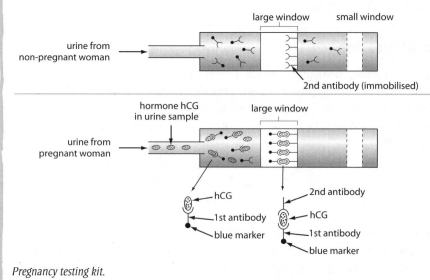

Pregnancy testing kit.

Sexual reproduction in plants

The flower is the organ of reproduction and usually contains both male and female parts. In angiosperms the female part, the ovule, is never exposed but is enclosed within a modified leaf, the carpel.

Structure of an insect-pollinated flower

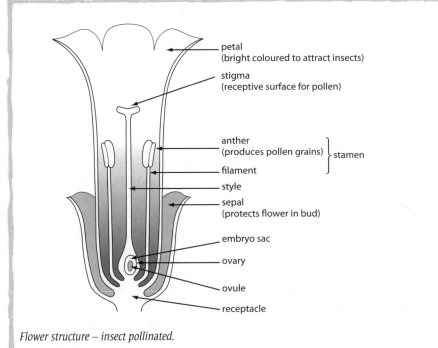

Flower structure – insect pollinated.

petal
(bright coloured to attract insects)

stigma
(receptive surface for pollen)

anther
(produces pollen grains) } stamen
filament

style

sepal
(protects flower in bud)

embryo sac

ovary

ovule

receptacle

Pollination

Pollination is the transfer of pollen grains from the anther to the stigma of a plant of the same species. Pollination is necessary so that the pollen grains, containing the male gametes, are brought into contact with the female part of the flower so that fertilisation can be achieved.

Self-pollination

In some species self-pollination occurs and the pollen from the anthers of a flower need only be transferred to the stigma of the same flower or another flower on the same plant.

Cross-pollination

In the majority of species cross-pollination occurs where pollen is transferred from the anthers of one flower to the stigma of another flower of the same species.

>> *Pointer*

Flowering plants or angiosperms are the most successful of all terrestrial plants. A key feature of their success is their relationship with animals, particularly insects. Pollen grains have no power of independent movement and have to be transferred to the female part of the flower to ensure fertilisation.

 **quickfire**

28 **Name the three parts that make up a carpel.**

Grade boost

Be prepared to label a diagram of a flower and explain the function of its parts.

quickfire

29 **State the difference between self- and cross-pollination.**

Grade boost

Different flowering plant species employ a variety of methods to ensure that cross-pollination takes place. These include the stamen and stigma ripening at different times, being at different levels within the flower, or there may be separate male and female flowers. You are not required to know any details of these methods.

>> *Pointer*

Candidates often confuse pollination and fertilisation. Make sure you understand the difference.

Grade boost

Link the genetic implications of pollination with previous work on meiosis.

quickfire

(30) Why do wind-pollinated flowers produce large quantities of pollen?

The genetic implications of self- and cross-pollination

Self-pollination results in in-breeding and a consequent reduction in the degree of variation in the population. There is also a greater chance of two undesirable recessive alleles being brought together at fertilisation.

However, there are advantages to inbreeding because it can preserve good genomes which may be suited to a relatively stable environment.

Therefore the two forms of pollination have very different genetic consequences:

- Self-pollination leads to self-fertilisation, cross-pollination to cross-fertilisation.
- Self-fertilised species depend on random assortment and crossing over during meiosis, and on mutation to bring about variation in the genomes of male and female gametes.
- Self-fertilised species display less genetic variation than cross-fertilised species that are produced from gametes from two different individuals.
- Out-breeding is of greater evolutionary significance because in the struggle for survival some genomes are more successful than others.

Flowers are adapted for cross-pollination by either insects or wind:

- In insect pollination, for example, bees feed on the sugary nectar using their long tongues to reach the nectar at the base of the female part of the flower. As the bee enters the flower, the anthers brush against the back of the bee leaving the sticky pollen behind. When the bee enters another flower, it brushes some of the pollen against the ripe stigma and cross-pollination has taken place.
- In wind-pollinated flowers the anthers hang outside the flower so that the wind can blow away the small, smooth and light pollen. The feathery stigmas hang outside the flowers and provide a large surface area for catching pollen grains that are blown into their path.

Insect-pollinated flowers	Wind-pollinated flowers
Colourful petals, scent and nectar	Small, green and inconspicuous, no scent, petals usually absent
Anthers within the flower	Anthers hanging outside the flower
Stigma within the flower	Large, feathery stigmas
Small quantities of sticky pollen	Large quantities of small, smooth, light pollen

The development of the sex cells and fertilisation

In the anther, diploid cells undergo meiosis to form haploid pollen grains. A pollen grain is surrounded by a tough wall that it resistant to desiccation. This enables pollen grains to be transferred from one flower to another without drying out.

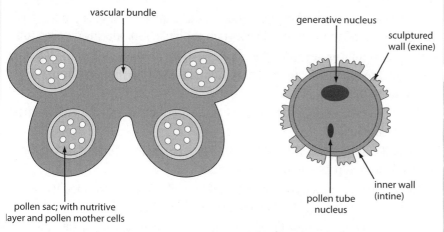

Pollen grain.

- Inside the pollen grain the haploid nucleus undergoes mitosis to produce two nuclei, a generative nucleus and a tube nucleus. The generative nucleus later gives rise to the two male nuclei.

- When the pollen is mature, the outer layers of the anthers dry out and tensions are set up in lateral grooves. Eventually dehiscence occurs and the edges of the pollen sacs curl away exposing the pollen grains. In insect-pollinated flowers these will be carried to the stigma by insects such as bees.

- The ovules are produced in the ovary with the female gamete or egg nucleus developing inside the ovule.

- In the female part of the flower a mother cell undergoes meiosis to produce a haploid embryo sac, within which eight nuclei form by mitosis. This is contained within the ovule. The ovule is contained within the ovary.

Mature ovule within the carpel.

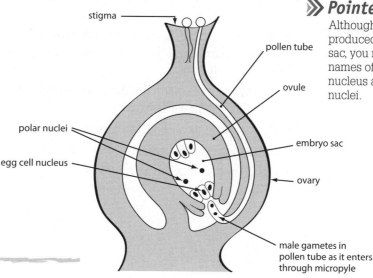

quickfire

㉛ State one way in which the pollen grain in the diagram is adapted for dispersal.

» Pointer

If asked to describe fertilisation you do not need to include a description of the development of the pollen grain.

Grade boost

Compare the processes of internal fertilisation in mammals with fertilisation in flowering plants.

Grade boost

In a given diagram be prepared to draw the pathway of growth of the pollen tube.

Grade boost

The ovule consists of the outer integuments surrounding an embryo sac containing the nuclei.

» Pointer

Although eight nuclei are produced in the embryo sac, you need know only the names of the female egg nucleus and the two polar nuclei.

③② What is the function of the pollen tube nucleus?

③③ What assists the growth of the pollen tube?

>> **Pointer**

Be clear about which nuclei fuse together. Consider using colours in a diagram to match nuclei that fuse.

③④ How is the triploid endosperm nucleus formed?

Grade boost

After the completion of fertilisation you should be able to describe the formation of the diploid and triploid nuclei, integuments, ovule and ovary.

③⑤ What is the difference between pollination and fertilisation?

Fertilisation

This is the process where a male gamete fuses with a female gamete to produce a zygote. In flowering plants the ovule is protected within the ovary. The male gamete is the nucleus contained in the pollen grain and can only reach the female nucleus in the ovule by means of a pollen tube.

- When a compatible pollen grain lands on the stigma, the stigma produces a sugary solution in which the pollen grain germinates, producing a pollen tube.
- The pollen tube grows down the style. It secretes enzymes as it goes, digesting its way through the tissues of the style. It may also gain nutrients from the digested products.
- The pollen tube nucleus is positioned at the tip of the tube, with the two male nuclei close behind.
- The pollen tube grows through the gap between the integuments, called the micropyle, and passes into the embryo sac.
- The pollen tube nucleus disintegrates presumably having completed its function of controlling the growth of the pollen tube.
- The tip of the pollen tube bursts open releasing the male gamete into the embryo sac and the two male nuclei enter.
- One of the male gametes fuses with the female nucleus to form a zygote.
- The other male gamete fuses with both polar nuclei to form a triploid endosperm nucleus.
- Thus, a double fertilisation occurs, a process unique to flowering plants.

Development of the fruit and seed

Following fertilisation, the development of the seed and fruit takes place. The seed develops from the fertilised ovule and contains an embryonic plant and a food store.

- The diploid zygote divides by mitosis to form the embryo, consisting of a plumule (developing shoot), a radicle (developing root) and one or two seed leaves or cotyledons.
- The triploid endosperm nucleus develops into a food store to provide reserves for the developing embryo.
- The integuments become the seed coat or testa.
- The ovule becomes the seed.
- The ovary becomes the fruit.

Structure of the seed

The broad bean is classed as a dicotyledon, as it has two seed leaves or cotyledons, whereas the maize is classed as a monocotyledon, as it has only one cotyledon. In the broad bean the food store has been absorbed into the cotyledons but in the maize, typically of cereal grains, the food store surrounds the seed leaves. The maize is in fact a fruit and not a seed.

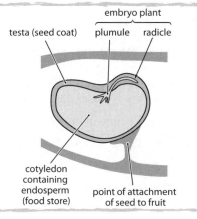

Broad bean seed (Vicia faba).

Germination of *Vicia faba*

After a period of dormancy and when environmental factors are favourable, stored food will be mobilised and the seed will germinate. The three main requirements for successful germination are:

- A suitable temperature – the optimum temperature for germination is the optimum for the enzymes involved in the process of germination. The temperature varies from species to species.
- Water – for mobilisation of enzymes, vacuolation of cells and for transport.
- Oxygen – respiration makes energy, in the form of ATP, available for metabolism and growth.

Mobilisation of food reserves during germination

- Food reserves in seeds are insoluble in water and cannot as such be transported in the seedling.
- The reserves must be broken down into relatively simple soluble substances which dissolve in water and are then transported to the growing apices of the young shoot or plumule and the young root or radicle.
- Water is taken up rapidly by the seed in the initial stages, causing the tissues to swell as well as mobilising the enzymes.
- The seed coat ruptures as the radicle pushes its way through first. The radicle will grow downwards and the plumule upwards.
- The enzyme, amylase, hydrolyses starch into maltose, which is transported to growing points.
- During germination the cotyledons of the broad bean remain below ground.
- The plumule is bent over in the shape of a hook as it pushes its way up through the soil. This protects the tip from damage by soil abrasion.
- If the seed has been planted at the correct depth in the soil, when the plumule emerges it unfurls and begins to make food for itself by photosynthesis. By now the food reserves in the cotyledons will have been depleted.

>> *Pointer*

Flowering plants are divided into two main groups: monocotyledons and dicotyledons. The monocotyledons are important as they include cereals.

36 Why do seeds require oxygen for germination?

37 Why does a seedling establish a root system in the early stages of development?

38 State the terms for 'young shoot' and 'young root'.

39 Explain what happens if a seed is planted too deeply in the soil.

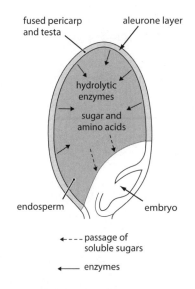

Maize fruit (Zea mays).

Inheritance

Key terms

Allele = the alternative form of a gene.

Gene = section of DNA on a chromosome coding for a particular polypeptide.

≫ Pointer

Gregor Mendel (1822–84) was the first person to work out the ways in which genes are inherited. He formulated two laws which form the basis of the science of genetics. This was an amazing feat as scientists of the time had no knowledge of DNA, genes or chromosomes.

≪ Grade boost

An understanding of genetics depends on the way chromosomes behave during meiosis. Consider referring back to page 60 before starting this topic.

Genes and alleles

- Genotype is the term that describes the genetic make-up of an organism. It also describes all the **alleles** that an organism contains.
- Phenotype is the observable characteristics of an organism.
- **Genes** have three main characteristics:
  - They can separate and combine.
  - They can mutate.
  - They code for the production of specific polypeptides.
- **Alleles** occupy a similar gene-position, or 'locus', on homologous chromosomes.
  - If a gene determines a particular inherited characteristic, the alleles which make up the gene may exist in two forms. For example, in a gene which determines fur colour in mice, the two alternative alleles may be for black and white fur. 'Black' and 'white' are the two alleles for the 'fur colour' gene.
- For any one locus on a chromosome, there are theoretically three different allele combinations.
  - Heterozygous – having different alleles for a given gene, that is, a dominant allele and a recessive allele are present together. Each of these alleles is carried on a different chromosome within a pair of homologous chromosomes.
  - Homozygous dominant – having the same two dominant alleles present for a given gene.
  - Homozygous recessive – having the same two recessive alleles present for a given gene.

In the simplest situations, a particular characteristic is controlled by a single gene. If an organism is heterozygous for this gene, the dominant allele will determine the form in which the characteristic is actually expressed. The outcome (that is the phenotype) of a heterozygous condition (that is, the genotype) will therefore be the same as that for a homozygous dominant condition.

Summary of genetic terms

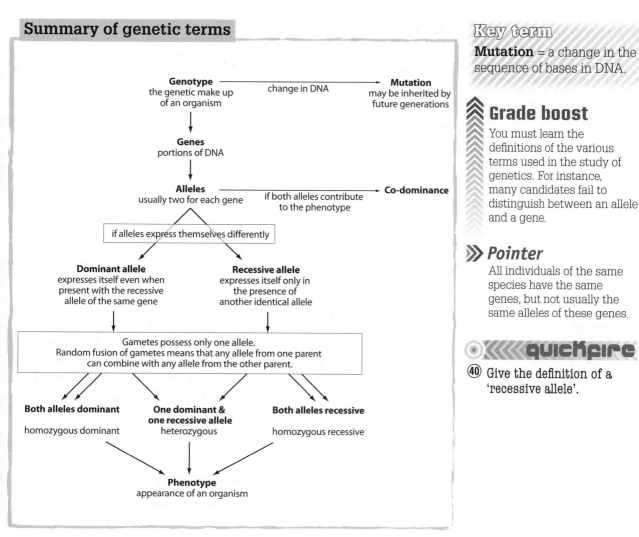

Key term

Mutation = a change in the sequence of bases in DNA.

Grade boost

You must learn the definitions of the various terms used in the study of genetics. For instance, many candidates fail to distinguish between an allele and a gene.

≫ Pointer

All individuals of the same species have the same genes, but not usually the same alleles of these genes.

40 Give the definition of a 'recessive allele'.

Monohybrid inheritance

The inheritance of a single pair of contrasting characters is known as monohybrid inheritance.

As a result of carrying out his experiments, Mendel formulated his first law of inheritance, the law of segregation, which states that:

'The characteristics of an organism are determined by factors (alleles) which occur in pairs. Only one of a pair of factors (alleles) can be present in a single gamete.'

≫ Pointer

Mendel's early experiments were based on selecting pea plants of two varieties which showed clearly separable characteristics such as tall and dwarf plants and round and wrinkled seeds.

≫ Pointer

Always follow instructions for carrying out a genetic cross. Once you have practised a number of crosses it is very easy to miss out stages or explanations. This may make your explanations impossible for others to follow. In an exam, even if you achieve the expected outcome, you may not gain full credit. So always carry out these instructions in their entirety.

≫ Pointer

In monohybrid crosses, two heterozygous individuals will produce offspring with a phenotypic ratio of 3:1.

≫ Pointer

In dihybrid crosses two heterozygous individuals will produce offspring with a phenotypic ratio of 9:3:3:1.

≋ Grade boost

You would be expected to state either of Mendel's first and second laws in an exam question.

Test cross or backcross

This is a method used in genetics to determine whether a particular dominant characteristic observed in an organism is determined by one or two dominant alleles.

For example, a prize black bull bought at a market by a farmer would be expected to be pure-breeding, homozygous dominant (BB). Or if not a pedigree bull it would be heterozygous (Bb). The phenotype is identical in both cases.

The backcross consists of crossing the bull with a known 'recessive' genotype, a white cow. (The double recessive phenotype has a known genotype because only one allele combination can produce it.)

If the resulting offspring are all black then the bull is pure-breeding or homozygous. If the resulting offspring include both white and black forms then the bull was heterozygous.

Dihybrid inheritance

This involves the inheritance of two separate genes. Mendel knew from his early experiments with monohybrid crosses that round seed shape was dominant to wrinkled, and that yellow colour was dominant to green. He used plants which differed by having two pairs of contrasting characters. He crossed homozygous pea plants with the two dominant characters, round and yellow seeds with homozygous plants with the two recessive characters, wrinkled and green. When plants grown from these seeds were self-pollinated the seeds produced were of four different types of shape and colour of seed coat. The four types are – round yellow, round green, wrinkled yellow and wrinkled green.

He also found that these types were in the ratio of approximately 9:3:3:1, proportions now known as the dihybrid ratio. This led Mendel to formulate his second law, which states that:

> 'Either one of a pair of contrasted characters may combine with either of another pair.'

With our present knowledge of genetics this statement can be rewritten as:

> 'Each member of an allelic pair may combine randomly with either of another pair.'

The genetic cross for Mendel's experiment may be represented as follows in the form of a Punnet square:

parental phenotypes	pure-breeding round yellow	pure-breeding wrinkled green
parental genotypes (2n)	**RRYY**	**rryy**
gametes (n)	all **RY**	all **ry**
F1 genotype (2n)	all **RrYy**	
F2 parental genotype	**RrYy**	**RrYy**
gametes (n)	**RY Ry rY ry**	**RY Ry rY ry**

R represents round seed (dominant)   **r** represents wrinkled (recessive)
Y represents yellow seed (dominant)   **y** represents green seed (recessive)

♀ \ ♂	**RY**	**Ry**	**rY**	**ry**
RY	**RY** **RY** round yellow	**Ry** **RY** round yellow	**rY** **RY** round yellow	**ry** **RY** round yellow
Ry	**RY** **Ry** round yellow	**Ry** **Ry** round green	**rY** **Ry** round yellow	**ry** **Ry** round green
rY	**RY** **rY** round yellow	**Ry** **rY** round yellow	**rY** **rY** wrinkled yellow	**ry** **rY** wrinkled yellow
ry	**RY** **ry** round yellow	**Ry** **ry** round green	**rY** **ry** wrinkled green	**ry** **rY** wrinkled green

F2 genotypes (2n) and phenotypes   **9** round yellow   **3** wrinkled yellow
                                        3 round green   **1** wrinkled green

Genetic cross.

>> *Pointer*

In an exam question you will usually be presented with the layout for your answer and also the letters to use to represent the characteristics. Use these letters, do not complicate the issue by using your own lettering.

㊶ Using the information, in the genetic cross between two heterozygous parents resulting in 96 offspring, what is the probability of the number of double recessive offspring, wrinkled and green?

A statistical test – Chi squared

The expected ratio of phenotypes in the offspring of a dihybrid cross is 9:3:3:1. This ratio represents the probability of getting these phenotypes. It would be surprising if the numbers came out exactly in this ratio. So how close do the observed results have to be to the expected, and have the differences between them happened by chance, or are they so different that something unexpected is taking place? To answer this question scientists use a statistical test called the Chi-squared test.

Consider the following F2 results obtained from the cross between plants with round, yellow seeds and those with wrinkled, green seeds described above.

Characteristic	Round, yellow	Round, green	Wrinkled, yellow	Wrinkled, green
Totals	315	108	101	32

Grade boost

The Chi² test is used to compare the observed results with those expected. It is a way of estimating the probability that differences between observed and expected results are due to chance alone and not some other factor influencing the results.

>> *Pointer*

This is the only statistical test you are required to use.

>> *Pointer*

The table has been completed on the next page.

≫ Pointer

The figures have been rounded for ease of calculation.

Grade boost

Why not practise using the statistical test by making up your own expected results, work out the Chi^2 and discover whether your results are significant or non-significant.

Statisticians carry out the following procedure:

1. Calculate the expected values (E).
   This is the total number of seeds divided by the number of possible types, for example, for round, yellow seeds $\dfrac{556 \times 9}{16} = 312.75$

2. Calculate the differences between the observed (O) and expected (E) results.

3. Square the differences.
   Use the formula $= \dfrac{\Sigma (O-E)^2}{E}$

4. Complete the table.

Phenotype	Observed (O)	Expected (E)	Difference (O–E)	$(O-E)^2$	$\dfrac{(O-E)^2}{E}$
Round, yellow	313	311	2.0	4	0.01
Round, green	108	104	-4.0	16	0.15
Wrinkled, yellow	101	104	-3.0	9	0.08
Wrinkled, green	32	35	3.0	9	0.26

5. Total the values in the last column.
   $0.01 + 0.15 + 0.08 + 0.26 = 0.50$

6. Work out the degrees of freedom. This is a measure of the spread of the data. It is always one less than the number of classes of data. In the example there are four different phenotype combinations, so there are three degrees of freedom.

7. To find out if this value is significant or non-significant it is necessary to use a Chi-squared table.

Number of classes	Degrees of freedom	Chi^2			
2	1	0.00	0.45	2.71	3.84
3	2	0.02	1.39	4.61	5.99
4	3	0.12	2.37	6.25	7.82
5	4	0.30	3.36	7.78	9.49
Probability that deviation is due to chance alone		0.99(99%)	0.50 (50%)	0.10 (10%)	0.05 (5%)

Statisticians consider that if the probability is greater than 5% the deviation is said to be non-significant. In other words, the deviation is due to chance alone. If the deviation is less than the 5% level, the deviation is said to be significant. That is, some factor other than chance is influencing the results.

8. Looking along the column for three degrees of freedom it can be seen that the Chi^2 value of 0.50 lies between 2.37 and 0.12 which is equivalent to a probability between 0.50 (50%) and 0.99 (99%). This means that the deviation from the 9:3:3:1 ratio is non-significant and is simply the result of statistical chance.

Co-dominance

Instead of one allele being dominant and the other recessive, both alleles are dominant, that is, the alleles express themselves equally in the phenotype.

In most cases the heterozygote shows a phenotype intermediate between those of the two homozygotes. Examples of co-dominance are:

- Snapdragon plants have the homozygous genotypes RR and WW and produce red or white flowers. However, if the two homozygous plants are crossed, the offspring are pink. That is, the two parents produce an intermediate offspring.
- Similarly, shorthorn cattle have the genotypes and phenotypes RR (red), RW (roan) and WW (white) coat colour.

The genetic diagram for these crosses is the same as that illustrating Mendel's first law but in the F1 all individuals have the intermediate phenotype.

There are two methods of representing the letters of the genotype:

	Method 1		Method 2	
Parental phenotypes	red flowers	× white flowers	red flower	× white flowers
Parental genotypes	R R	W W	$C^R C^R$	$C^W C^W$
Gametes	R	W	C^R	C^W
F1 genotype	R W		$C^R C^W$	
F1 phenotype	All pink			

Sex determination

Humans have 46 chromosomes arranged in 23 pairs. The first 22 pairs are the autosomes; the last pair are the sex chromosomes.

- In humans the male has a dissimilar pair of sex chromosomes, called **X** and **Y**, whilst the female has a pair of two similar **X** chromosomes.
- All the female's eggs contain an **X** chromosome.
- Half the male's sperm contains an **X** chromosome and the other half contains a **Y** chromosome.
- At fertilisation the egg may join with either an **X** sperm or a **Y** sperm. This gives an equal chance of the child being a boy or a girl.

Parental phenotype:	male	female
Parental genotypes:	**XY**	**XX**
Gametes:	**XY**	**X**

		Male gametes	
		X	**Y**
Female gametes	**X**	**XX**	**XY**
	X	**XX**	**XY**

Offspring phenotypes: 50% male

50% female

>> *Pointer*
The monohybrid and dihybrid crosses considered so far involve alleles that are either dominant or recessive. Sometimes both alleles are expressed and neither is dominant.

>> *Pointer*
You are not expected to memorise examples of co-dominance. In an exam question you will be told that co-dominance is involved.

Grade boost
In snapdragon plants one allele codes for an enzyme that catalyses the formation of red pigment in flowers. The other allele codes for an altered enzyme, which lacks this catalytic activity and so does not produce the pigment.

>> *Pointer*
Use different letters, such as R and W, when answering questions on co-dominance. Different books suggest different methods of representing the letters.

Grade boost

As the X chromosome is much longer than the Y chromosome, for most of the length of the former there is no equivalent portion of the Y chromosome.

quickfire

(42) What is meant by the phrase 'a gene is sex linked'?

▶▶ Pointer

Haemophilia is an example of a sex-linked trait in humans.

▶▶ Pointer

The males have a Y chromosome and this could only have been inherited from their fathers. Their X chromosome must therefore have come from their mothers.

Sex linkage

Some alleles are carried on the X chromosome, so they are described as sex linked.

- The Y chromosome is much smaller than the X and carries very few genes. Therefore in the male any recessive genes carried on the X chromosome will express themselves in the phenotype. This is because they are unpaired and so there is no dominant gene present. This special form of inheritance is known as sex linkage, an important feature of which is that the male cannot hand on the gene to his sons as they must receive the Y chromosome to become male. On the other hand, all his daughters must receive the recessive gene from him. Females who are heterozygous for sex-linked recessive traits are known as carriers and have a 50% chance of handing on the recessive to their sons.

Haemophilia is caused by a recessive allele on the X chromosome. The gene that codes for Factor VIII, an important protein involved in blood clotting, is a sex-linked gene located on the X chromosome.

- Haemophilia is a potentially lethal condition. It is the result of an individual being unable to produce one of the many clotting factors. The inability of the blood to clot leads to slow and persistent bleeding.
- It is now possible to extract the particular clotting factor from donated blood allowing haemophiliacs to lead near-normal lives. (Although the risk of passing the disease on to their children remains.)
- This condition occurs almost exclusively in males.
- When the recessive allele occurs in males it expresses itself because the Y chromosome cannot carry any corresponding dominant allele.
- For the condition to arise in females it requires the double recessive state and as the recessive allele is relatively rare in the population this is unlikely to occur.
- To obtain an affected female, the father must be affected and the mother either affected or a carrier.

If **H** is the allele for normal blood clotting, h is the allele for haemophilia.

The possible genotypes are:

$X^H X^H$ female, normal

$X^H X^h$ female carrier

$X^h X^h$ female haemophiliac

$X^H Y$ male, normal

$X^h Y$ male, haemophiliac

Consider a cross between a normal female and a haemophiliac male.

Parental genotypes: $X^H X^H \times X^h Y$

Gametes: $X^H \times X^h Y$

		Male gametes	
		X^h	Y
Female gametes	X^H	$X^H X^h$	$X^H Y$
	X^H	$X^H X^h$	$X^H Y$

Offspring phenotypes: 50% carrier females

50% normal males

Linkage

Mendel was fortunate in his choice of characters in pea plants because these particular characters are controlled by single genes. Pea plants are either tall or dwarf, flower colours are clear-cut and easy to tell apart.

However, linked genes on the same chromosome pass into the gamete and then into the offspring together. The crosses and ratios considered so far have involved two pairs of contrasting characters found on *different* chromosomes. Crosses involving linkage do not follow the typical Mendelian pattern. These ratios will not be obtained if the genes are found on the *same* chromosome.

Recombination takes place when alleles are exchanged between homologous chromosomes as a result of crossing over. The further apart two genes are on a chromosome, the more chance there is of crossing over taking place.

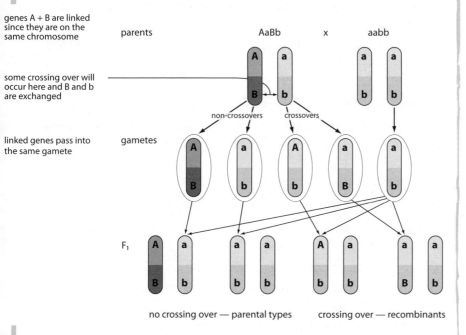

genes A + B are linked since they are on the same chromosome

some crossing over will occur here and B and b are exchanged

linked genes pass into the same gamete

Crossing over.

In meiosis linked genes are passed on together to the gametes so that most of the F2 progeny inherit the characteristics determined by the linked genes. When crossing over occurs, an opportunity is provided for linked genes to be separated and give rise to recombinants. However, crossing over may take place in only a small proportion of the cells undergoing meiosis, between 5 and 10%. Therefore few of the gametes will contain recombinant genes.

>> **Pointer**

Linkage takes place when two different genes are located on the same chromosome. The genes are inherited together, because they move together during meiosis and appear in the same gamete.

>> **Pointer**

In an exam question you would normally be told that linkage was taking place.

▲ **Grade boost**

If crossing over did not occur, only two types of offspring would be possible.

◉ ⟨⟨⟨⟨ **quickpire**

43 Approximately what percentage of recombinants would you expect from a cross of linked genes?

④④ Explain why gene mutations rarely show up in the phenotype.

④⑤ Suggest why bacteria are used widely in mutation experiments.

Grade boost

Although mutations occur randomly, they occur with a set frequency. The rate varies from species to species but is typically one mutation per 100,000 genes per generation.

Grade boost

Mutations arise spontaneously during DNA replication.

It is incorrect to say that mutagens cause mutations. Increased exposure to mutagens increases the *rate* of mutations occurring.

④⑥ Name one mutagen.

④⑦ What term is applied to a mutagen that causes cancer?

④⑧ Name the two forms of mutation.

Mutations

A mutation is a change in the amount, arrangement or structure in the DNA of an organism.

- It may affect a single gene or a whole chromosome.
- Most mutations occur in somatic (body) cells.
- Only those mutations which occur in the formation of gametes can be inherited.
- Mutations are spontaneous random events which may provide a source of material for natural selection pressures and therefore evolution.
- Mutation rates are normally very small, therefore mutation has less impact on evolution than other sources of variation.
- In general, organisms with short life cycles and more frequent meiosis show a greater rate of mutation.
- The rate of mutations occurring can be increased by ionising radiation and mutagenic chemicals.

Mutagens and the mutation rate

Mutations happen naturally. However, scientists have found that the mutation rate is increased if organisms are exposed to mutagens. These are factors in the environment which include:

- X-rays, gamma radiation and UV light.
- Chemicals, such as polycyclic hydrocarbons in cigarette smoke.

A mutagen which causes cancer is a carcinogen.

Mutations can happen in two ways:

1. DNA is not copied properly before cell division.
   - Sometimes mistakes are made in the copying process so that new chromosomes are faulty.
   - Usually they are small errors, involving only one gene, so they are called gene mutations or point mutations.
2. Chromosomes are damaged and break.
   - If chromosomes break they will normally repair themselves (the DNA will rejoin) but they may not repair themselves correctly. This can lead to large changes in the structure of the DNA and may affect a large number of genes. These are called chromosome mutations.

Gene mutations

A change in the structure of a DNA molecule, producing a different allele of a gene, is a gene mutation. Any gene can mutate but rates vary from one gene to another within an organism. Gene mutations are changes in the base pairs within the genes. They can take the form of duplication, insertion, deletion, inversion or substitution of bases. Whatever the change, the result is the formation of a modified polypeptide.

How can mutations cause a change in the phenotype?

- The genetic code, which ultimately determines an organism's characteristics, is made up of a specific sequence of nucleotides on the DNA molecule.

- Any change to one or more of these nucleotides, or any rearrangement of the sequence, will produce the incorrect sequence of amino acids in the protein it makes.

- The protein made is often an enzyme which may then be unable to catalyse a specific reaction. For example, a specific enzyme is necessary to convert a chemical precursor into the skin pigment, melanin. If a gene mutation results in the inability to produce this enzyme, the organism will lack a pigment. The organism is referred to as an albino.

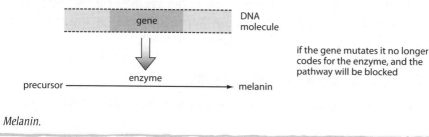

Melanin.

Sickle-cell anaemia

A gene mutation (substitution) in the gene producing haemoglobin results in a defect called sickle-cell anaemia. The replacement of just one base in the DNA molecule results in the wrong amino acid being incorporated into two of the polypeptide chains which make up the haemoglobin molecule. The abnormal haemoglobin causes red blood cells to become sickle-shaped. These abnormal shaped red blood cells are less able to carry oxygen, resulting in anaemia and possible death. Haemoglobin S is produced instead of normal haemoglobin by a single base chain that causes valine to be substituted for glutamic acid at the sixth position in the β globulin chain. DNA codes for glutamic acid are CTT or CTC. Two of the codes for valine are CAT and CAC. In either case the substitution of A for T as the second base would bring about the formation of haemoglobin S.

The mutant gene is co-dominant. In the homozygous state the individual suffers the disease but in the heterozygous state the individual has 30–40% sickle cells, the rest are normal. The heterozygous condition is referred to as sickle-cell trait.

>> *Pointer*

You are not expected to know about the different forms of gene mutation.

Grade boost

A modified polypeptide means that it will not be able to perform its intended function in the cell.

quickfire

⑭⑨ What are the chances of two parents with sickle-cell trait having a child with sickle-cell anaemia?

>> *Pointer*

Bases and amino acids are named in the description of sickle-cell anaemia. These are used to illustrate the points being made and you would not be expected to remember these.

Chromosome mutations

These are mutations that cause changes in the structure or number of whole chromosomes in cells. They are most likely to occur during meiosis, when the process can go wrong as the paired chromosomes line up on the crowded equator at metaphase and are pulled apart in anaphase. Errors can result in the chromosomes not being shared equally between the daughter cells.

Changes in structure

During prophase I of meiosis, homologous chromosomes pair up and exchange of material takes place at chiasmata. Errors arise when chromosomes rejoin with the corresponding pieces of chromosome on its homologous partner. Often the homologous chromosomes end up with a different gene sequence. This makes it impossible for pairing up in meiosis to take place.

Changes in numbers

Non-disjunction is a process in which faulty cell division means that one of the daughter cells receives two copies of a chromosome while the other gets none. In Down's syndrome chromosome number 21 is affected. If this happens in an ovary, it results in an oocyte with either no chromosome 21 or with two copies instead of one. Oocytes with no chromosome 21 die but those with two copies survive and may be fertilised. The resulting zygote has three chromosome 21s with a total of 47 chromosomes. This condition is known as trisomy 21 and the zygote will develop into a child with Down's syndrome.

Changes in sets of chromosomes

Occasionally a mutation can affect whole sets of chromosomes. This is known as polyploidy.

A defect in meiosis may result in a gamete receiving two sets of chromosomes. When this diploid gamete is fertilised by a normal haploid gamete the zygote will be triploid, that is, having three sets of chromosomes. If two diploid gametes fuse then a tetraploid will be produced. Tetraploidy may also happen after fertilisation if, during mitosis, the two sets of chromosomes double but fail to separate.

Polyploidy is common in flowering plants and is associated with beneficial characteristics. Tomatoes and wheat are polyploids. Triploids are usually sterile as they cannot form homologous pairs.

Grade boost

Down's syndrome occurs in approximately one in 700 births and the incidence of the mutation is related to the age of the mother, a result of the higher chance of mutation occurring during the formation of oocytes in older ovaries.

quickfire

(50) During micropropagation of cauliflowers the number of chromosomes in the cells of some of the plants produced is 36 and not 18 as in the parent plant. Suggest:
(a) How the number of chromosomes has doubled.
(b) Why the cauliflower plants, that have three of each chromosome type in each of their cells, are sterile.

Why are mutations important?

Mutations are important because they increase variation in a population. Most mutations are harmful to the organism concerned. Beneficial mutations are very rare but they may give a selective advantage to an organism.

- If a mutation is in a body cell, it may cause cancer. For example, increased exposure to UV light is linked to skin cancer.

- If the mutation is in a gamete, it will not affect the individual producing the gamete, but will affect the zygote that develops from it, that is, the offspring.

- These mutations cause sudden and distinct differences between individuals. They are therefore the basis of discontinuous variation.

- There are potential advantages from mutations that are beneficial and may increase variation. However, most mutations are recessive to the normal allele. A recessive mutant allele must await replication in the gene pool over many generations before chance brings recessive alleles together, resulting in their expression.

Carcinogens

Substances that cause cancer are called carcinogens. These affect the DNA in cells, resulting in mutations.

Mutations that occur in body or somatic cells often have no effect on an organism. Most mutated cells are recognised as foreign by the body's immune system and are destroyed.

Occasionally the mutation may affect the regulation of cell division. Cancers are thought to start when changes take place in these genes. If a cell with such a mutation escapes the attack of the immune system, it can produce a lump of cells called a tumour. Tumours are usually harmless or benign but sometimes the tumour cells are able to spread around the body and invade other tissues. This type of tumour is described as malignant and the diseases caused by such tumours are cancers.

- Tobacco smoke contains a number of harmful chemicals that affect human health. These include tar, nicotine and carbon monoxide. Tar is a mixture of many toxic chemicals. It collects in the lungs as the tobacco smoke cools. Tar contains carcinogens which affect the DNA in the cells of the alveoli.

- Normally, genes control cell division and division is halted when sufficient cells have been produced for growth and repair.

- Tumour suppressor genes normally inhibit cell division. Carcinogens in tobacco smoke cause these genes to mutate, so that they do not carry out their normal function, leading to uncontrolled cell division.

- **Oncogenes** and mutated suppressor genes can both lead to lung cancer. About 25% of all cancer deaths in developed countries are due to carcinogens in the tar of tobacco smoke.

Key term
Oncogene = a mutated gene that causes cancer.

Grade boost
Mutations arising in body cells are not passed on to the next generation. Only mutations occurring during the formation of gametes are inherited.

Pointer
Any agent that causes cancer is called a carcinogen and is described as carcinogenic. Therefore some mutagens are carcinogenic.

quickfire

51 Which chemical in tobacco smoke contains carcinogens?

Variation and evolution

Types of variation

Continuous variation

Grade boost

Variety in asexually reproducing organisms can only be increased by mutation. Sexually reproducing organisms increase variation as a result of meiosis, fusion of gametes in addition to mutations.

Most characters are controlled by a number of genes and the differences in the character are not clear cut. A character within a population showing a gradation from one extreme to another shows continuous variation. An example is height. If an individual has inherited a number of alleles for tallness from the parents, that individual has the potential to grow tall.

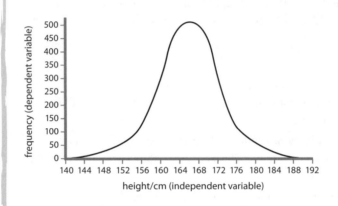

Normal distribution curve.

52 Is the presence or absence of ear lobes an example of continuous or discontinuous variation?

Discontinuous variation

Characters that are clear-cut and easy to tell apart are controlled by a single gene. There are no intermediate types. For example, light and dark forms in the peppered moth, the ABO blood grouping system, where the gene has more than two alleles.

Grade boost

Environmental factors also play a part played in a characteristic such as height. Individuals that are genetically predetermined to be the same height actually grow to different heights due to variations in environmental factors such as diet.

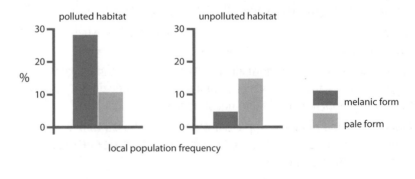

Discontinuous variation.

Origins of variation

Variation arises in two ways:

1. Non-heritable variation or environmental influences:

   - The environment has a role in determining phenotypic variation. Environmental factors in humans may include diet and exercise, whereas plants are affected by temperature, light and available nutrients.

   - An organism will inherit genes, giving it a theoretical maximum size, but whether or not this is reached will depend upon nutrition during the growth period and other environmental factors. Thus, if organisms of identical genotype are subject to different environmental influences, they show considerable variety. Because these influences are varied, they are largely responsible for continuous variation in a population.

2. Heritable variation

   Much more important to evolution is inherited variation that results from genetic changes. As a result of sexual reproduction, variation may be increased when the genotype of one parent is mixed with that of the other. The sexual process has three inbuilt methods of creating variety:

   - The mixing of two different parental genotypes where cross-fertilisation occurs.

   - The random distribution of chromosomes during metaphase I of meiosis.

   - The crossing over between homologous chromosomes during prophase I of meiosis.

   Although these processes may establish a new combination of alleles in one generation, it is mutations that generate long-lasting variations of a novel kind. However, as previously stated, the occurrence of a useful mutation is a very rare event.

53 How may genetic variation be increased in asexually reproducing organisms?

>> *Pointer*
Variations due to the effect of the environment have little evolutionary significance as they are not passed from one generation to the next.

54 Apart from mutations, list three sources of variation.

Inter- and intra-specific competition for breeding success and survival

- All organisms have the reproductive potential to increase their populations, although they rarely do so.

- As a population increases, various environmental factors come into play to keep the numbers down.

- Organisms must compete for limited resources. For example, plants compete for light, space, mineral ions; animals compete for food, shelter, etc.

There are two types of competition:

- Intra-specific competition – competition between individuals of the same species. This is the basis of the origin of species by natural selection.

- Inter-specific competition – competition between individuals of different species is illustrated by predator–prey relationships.

Key terms

Gene pool = the total number of alleles in a population at any one time.

Population = a group of interbreeding individuals of the same species, occupying the same habitat at the same time.

≫ Pointer

The number of young produced is far greater than the number which will survive to become adults. Many young die before maturity and so do not reproduce.

 quickfire

55 What is meant by the term 'selection pressure'?

≫ Pointer

Selection pressures increase the chances of some alleles being passed on to the next generation, and decrease the chance of others being inherited.

Selection pressure

What determines which individuals die and which survive? Is it a matter of luck or are some individuals born with a better chance of survival than others? Variation within a population of organisms means that some will have characteristics that give them an advantage in the 'struggle for survival'.

In rabbits, coat colour may vary. Most rabbits have alleles which give the normal brown colour. A small number may be homozygous for the recessive allele which gives a white coat. A white rabbit will stand out and is more likely to be killed by a predator such as a fox. As the white rabbit is unlikely to survive to become a mature adult, the chances of it reproducing and passing on its allele for white coat are very small. The allele for white coat will remain rare in the population. However, in the arctic winter, the disadvantage becomes an advantage.

Predation by foxes is an example of a selection pressure. The effect of such selection pressures on the frequency of alleles in a population is called natural selection. Predation increases 'fitness' in the prey. For example, foxes kill the weakest rabbits.

Selection, in the context of evolution, is the process by which organisms that are better adapted to their environment survive and breed, while those less well adapted fail to do so. These better adapted organisms are more likely to pass on their characteristics to succeeding generations. The organism's environment exerts a selection pressure and this determines the spread of any allele within the **gene pool**.

Population genetics

A **population** of organisms reproducing sexually contains a large amount of genetic variation. All the alleles of all the genes of all the individuals in a population at any one time are known as the gene pool.

Population genetics is concerned with determining the relative proportions of the various genotypes present in a population, from which can be calculated the relative proportions of alleles in the population. This is known as allele frequency.

Each organism contains just one of the many possible sets of genes that can be formed from the pool. The gene pool remains stable if the environment is stable. However, if the environment changes, some phenotypes will be advantageous and will be selected for, whilst others will be disadvantageous and will be selected against. Thus a gene pool is constantly changing, some alleles becoming more frequent and others less frequent. In some circumstances alleles may be totally lost from the gene pool.

Certain factors can act upon a genetic equilibrium and bring about significant changes to the frequency of some of the genes and change the composition of the gene pool. These factors include genetic drift, mutations and natural selection.

Genetic drift may be an important evolutionary mechanism in small or isolated populations.

Say an allele occurs in 1% of the members of a species. In a large population, of say 1,000,000, then 10,000 individuals may be expected to possess the allele. By chance, the population of individuals with the allele will not be significantly altered in the next generation. If, however, the population is much smaller, say 1000 individuals, only one will carry the allele. By chance, this one may fail to mate and pass on the allele and so it will be lost from the population altogether.

An important case of genetic drift is when a few individuals become isolated from the rest of the species and start a new population; for example, when a few individuals colonise an isolated island or some new habitat. These founder members of the new population are a small sample of the population from which they originated. By chance they may have a very different gene frequency. While the founder population remains small, it may undergo genetic drift and become even more different from the large parental population. This process is called the founder effect. The effect undoubtedly contributed to the evolutionary divergence of Darwin's finches after strays from the South American mainland reached the remote Galapagos Islands.

Evolution and selection

Charles Darwin (1809–1882) was employed as a naturalist and member of a scientific survey which sailed to South America and Australia in 1832. He visited a small group of volcanic islands called the Galapagos Islands. These are situated about 600 miles off the coast of Ecuador. When these islands were originally formed by volcanic activity, no life existed there. Any plants or animals must have reached the islands by sea or air from the mainland. Darwin studied many different animals on the islands and was amazed by the variety of life-forms that existed there.

Darwin's observations of variation within a population and the tendency for the adult population to be stable in size led to the development of the idea of **natural selection**. The theory proposes that those organisms that are better adapted to their environment are more likely to survive and reproduce to produce offspring that are successful.

The theory is based on the following observations:

- In any population there is variation.
- Individuals within a population have the potential to produce large numbers of offspring, yet the number of adults tends to stay the same from one generation to the next.

From these observations, two deductions were made:

- There is a struggle for survival (competition) with only the 'fittest' surviving.
- The individuals that survive and reproduce pass on to their offspring the characteristics that enable them to succeed (that is, a selective advantage).

Key terms

Evolution = the process by which new species are formed from pre-existing ones over a long period of time.

Natural selection = a process that encourages the transmission of favourable alleles and hinders the transmission of unfavourable ones so contributing to evolution.

>> *Pointer*

To this point a study has been made of how genes and alleles are passed between individuals in a population. This section considers the genes and alleles of an entire population.

>> *Pointer*

You are not required to study the Hardy-Weinberg principle.

>> *Pointer*

Unless an allele leads to a phenotype with an advantage or a disadvantage compared with other phenotypes, its allele frequency in a population will remain constant from one generation to the next.

>> *Pointer*

Darwin found evidence of adaptive radiation in the finch population. This is studied in BY2.

Key terms

Isolation = occurs when a barrier prevents two populations from breeding with one another.

Speciation = the evolution of new species from existing species.

Species = a group of similar organisms that can interbreed to produce fertile offspring.

>> *Pointer*

Darwin proposed natural selection as the force that causes changes within populations.

㊋ State why population numbers remain constant despite the production of large numbers of offspring.

㊌ What is meant by geographical isolation?

🔺 **Grade boost**

Candidates tend to waffle in their responses to this topic. The learning of definitions is essential and the use of a model helps focus on the concept.

In time, a group of individuals that once belonged to the same species may give rise to two different groups that are sufficiently distinct to belong to two separate species.

If the environment or conditions change, then the features needed to survive in it will change, so natural selection is a continuous process.

Isolation and speciation

Speciation

Within a population of one **species** there are groups of interbreeding individuals. Within each population there are breeding sub-units called demes. Individuals within a deme tend to breed with each other more often than they do with individuals of other demes. New species arise when some barrier to reproduction occurs so that the gene pool is divided and the flow of genes between separate demes may cease. Such a barrier, which effectively prevents gene exchange between demes, is called an isolating mechanism. If the separation is long term, eventually the two groups will be so different that two new species incapable of interbreeding are formed. The separate species will each have their own gene pool. This process is called **speciation**.

Isolation leading to speciation

For new species to develop from a population, some form of isolating mechanism is required. There are two main forms of isolating mechanisms:

Geographical isolation

This occurs when the population becomes physically split into separate demes. The physical barrier may be a mountain or a river or any feature which prevents the population of the same species from interbreeding. The evolution of a new species is very probable, given time. This sort of speciation is known as allopatric speciation.

Consider an isolation model:

- A population of birds with short flight range feed and breed only in the cool conditions of a valley and the lower slopes of two mountains a considerable distance apart. The birds are only able to breed at a certain temperature provided by the cool conditions. The mountain peaks are too cold for the birds to survive.

- The climate then changes and it gets warmer. The birds tend to inhabit the nearest mountain and become confined to the cool mountain peaks. The birds are split into two separate breeding populations or demes, each with their own gene pool. Over a very prolonged period of isolation the birds may be subjected to different selection pressures. Because of the effect of natural selection on each gene pool, the two populations may become sufficiently genetically different to prevent interbreeding.

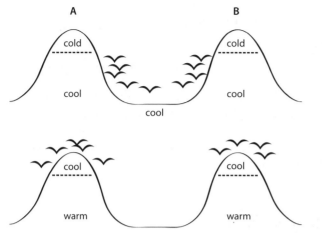

Isolation model.

- It may be that those birds isolated on mountain top A adapted to feed on insects in crevices. Birds with long beaks fed successfully and so survived to reproduce and passed on this favourable characteristic. On mountain top B the birds had fruit on which to feed and so had a different beak type.

- If the climate reverts to the original temperature and the birds are again able to inhabit the valley and lower mountain slopes, they come into contact with each other. Over time the appearance may have altered and the different shaped beaks may result in a different mating call. The birds are no longer attracted to each other. If the two populations have established a different gene pool and can no longer interbreed, then two separate species have evolved.

Reproductive isolation

When organisms inhabiting the same area become reproductively isolated into two groups when there are no physical barriers. Species formation occurring in demes in the same geographic area is known as sympatric speciation.

The barriers to breeding include the following mechanisms:

- Behavioural isolation – in animals with elaborate courtship behaviour, the steps in the display of one subspecies fail to attract the necessary response in a potential partner of another subspecies.

- Mechanical isolation – the genitalia of the two groups may be incompatible.

- Gametic isolation – in flowering plants pollination may be prevented because the pollen grain fails to germinate on the stigma, whereas in animals sperm may fail to survive in the oviduct of the partner.

- **Hybrid** unviability – despite fertilisation taking place, development of the embryo may not occur. This may be because the chromosomes no longer match each other, as is the case with polyploidy.

- Hybrid sterility – when individuals of different species breed, the sets of chromosomes from each parent are different. These sets are unable to pair up during meiosis and so the offspring are unable to produce gametes. The hybrid is therefore sterile and the species is reproductively isolated.

Key term

Hybrid = the offspring resulting from cross breeding of different species.

Grade boost

Darwin considered that species gradually change over long periods of time from one form to another. It would then be expected that biologists would find intermediate forms between one fossil species and the next in successive rock strata. However, these forms are surprisingly rare and this has led some biologists to believe that new species may arise relatively rapidly (perhaps within a few thousand years) and then remain unchanged for millions of years before changing again.

Grade boost

An example of hybrid sterility is a 'zebronkey'. This is the name given to the offspring which results from the mating of a zebra with a donkey. The zebronkey is sterile as it has 53 pairs of chromosomes that are unable to form homologous pairs.

Applications of reproduction and genetics

In the past, conventional breeding techniques have been used to improve farm animals, crop and ornamental plants. However, selection and cross breeding is laborious, time consuming and sometimes unpredictable. In the future the quality of farm animals may be improved by laboratory-based breeding techniques involving embryos.

Cloning of animals

Key term

Clone = a group of genetically identical organisms formed from a single parent as a result of asexual reproduction or by artificial means.

quickfire

⑤⑧ State the term used to describe the mother that receives a transplanted embryo.

》 Pointer

The technique of embryo surgery has enabled farmers to increase their stock. It is also used to conserve rare breeds, where embryos of young animals are bisected and successfully transplanted into a surrogate mother of a common breed to produce a new individual of the rare type.

Embryo cloning

This technique has been used to produce genetically identical individuals and has made it possible for farmers to increase the numbers of their animals. Eggs are taken from high milk yielding cows and are fertilised in a petri dish using sperm from the best bulls. This is known as *in vitro* fertilisation (commonly called 'test-tube fertilisation'). The fertilised egg divides to form a ball of cells. This group of cells or young embryos are split into separate cells. Each of these cells will then develop into a new embryo, genetically identical (**clone**) to the original. The embryos are then transplanted into other cows called surrogates.

Stages in embryo cloning.

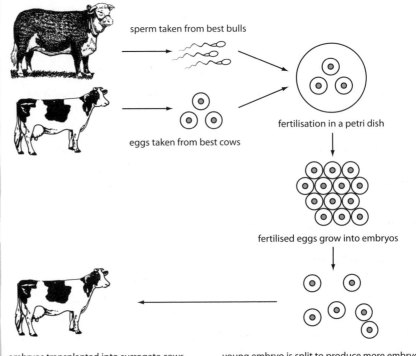

sperm taken from best bulls

eggs taken from best cows

fertilisation in a petri dish

fertilised eggs grow into embryos

embryos transplanted into surrogate cows

young embryo is split to produce more embryos

Cloning by nuclear transplants

This technique allows clones to be produced from one individual. It involves transplanting a nucleus from a somatic or body cell into an egg cell. The following describes the procedure:

- Cells are taken from the tissues of the udder of a sheep (the donor) and cultured in a medium which stops division.

- An unfertilised egg is removed from a different sheep (the recipient) and the nucleus is removed, leaving an egg cell without a nucleus.

- The donor and recipient cells are fused together using a gentle electric pulse, and allowed to divide, producing a ball of cells.

- The developing embryo is implanted into the uterus of another sheep (the host or surrogate).

- The lamb born is genetically identical to the original donor sheep.

59 Suggest why it would be undesirable to produce all farm animals by cloning.

60 State one advantage of the cloning of animals.

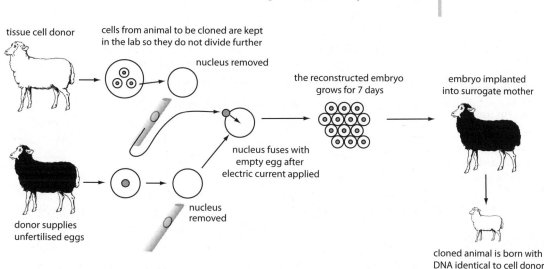

Cloning by nuclear transfer.

This technique has enabled desirable qualities to be preserved for future generations. Embryo cloning allows many genetically identical copies of an animal to be produced. If a high milk yield mutation occurred in a cow, making her significantly better than other members of the herd, cross breeding with a bull would reshuffle her genes with a consequent loss of her unique characteristic. Cloning is the only technique that will conserve her unique features for future generations.

The advantages of cloning in animals:

- Cell culture is useful for production of cells in quantity, e.g. cancer cells for medical research, monoclonal antibodies.

- The production of a single, identical, genetic line of cells with desirable characteristics may be used to maintain genetic stocks.

Key terms

Differentiate = cells become specialised for different functions.

In vitro = refers to experiments carried on outside the living body, that is, in the laboratory.

Stem cell = an undifferentiated cell capable of dividing to give rise to cells which can develop into different types of specialised cells.

≫ Pointer

Cell cultures have been used for some time for medical and research purposes, for example in the culture of viruses for vaccine production and also in the production of monoclonal antibodies.

New techniques such as cell replacement therapy and tissue engineering are being developed.

quickfire

⑥¹ State one medical application of tissue culture.

The disadvantages of cloning in animals:

- In mammals the technique is very expensive and unreliable.
- There may be the inadvertent selection of disadvantageous alleles.
- Progeny may show long-term/unforeseen effects such as premature ageing.

Tissue culture

Cells from young animals and cancer cells can be induced to divide **in vitro**. A few cells retain their ability to divide even in an adult, for example new cells to heal wounds. Most cells, however, **differentiate** into cells which have specific functions, such as nerve or muscle cells, and most of these specialised cells do not normally divide again.

- The technique of growing cells in a laboratory is called tissue culture. The medium, in which the cells are grown, has to be precisely controlled, and conditions such as water potential and temperature have to be carefully monitored. Animal cells in tissue culture develop into mature cells of the same type as the cell from which the culture was started. Of course, all the cells are identical and contain identical genes to the parent cell.

- Tissue engineering involves inducing living cells to grow on a framework of synthetic material to produce a tissue such as skin tissue. This has obvious applications for the treatment of extensive, deep burns. An artificial skin called 'Apligraf' is now widely used in place of skin grafts.

- Other applications of tissue engineering include blood vessel replacement, bone and cartilage repair, and the treatment of degenerative nerve diseases. Central to this area of research is the use of **stem cells**. The best sources of these cells are from very early embryos, also some adult tissues, such as bone marrow, contain stem cells. Therapeutic stem cell cloning has enormous medical potential. Cloned stem cells could be used to generate organs for transplantation. This would prevent immune rejection and reduce the problem of organ shortages.

The technique may be described in simple terms as follows:

- A mature cell is taken from the patient and the nucleus is removed.
- The nucleus is removed from a human ovum.
- The mature cell nucleus is transferred into the 'empty' ovum.
- The ovum, containing the patient's DNA, divides to form a ball of stem cells.
- Stem cells are isolated and cultured with appropriate growth factors, allowing them to grow into the required organ or tissue.

In vitro fertilisation

Over the last 25 years there has been a tremendous increase in the number of couples seeking help to conceive a child. A couple are described as infertile if they have failed to conceive after 12 months. A couple seeking fertility treatment will first be assessed to try to discover the cause of the problem. Causes in the UK:

- 50% are the result of problems with the female's reproductive system.
- 35% are related to the male.
- 15% cannot be explained.

The technique involves:

- Ovulation is stimulated using hormones at a specific dosage which aims to cause several follicles to develop at the same time.
- The oocytes are collected from the female using a tube inserted through the vagina and into the oviducts. Ultrasound is used to guide the tube.
- On the same day, the male's semen is collected and placed in liquid containing nutrients.
- Each oocyte is placed in a separate dish and about 100,000 sperm are added to each. (An alternate method involves injecting the sperm DNA into an oocyte.)
- Three days later the oocytes are examined to see which ones have been fertilised. Two are selected, to increase the chance that at least one will implant, and inserted into the uterus using a tube.

Ethics and the use of stem cells

There is considerable controversy surrounding this area of research.

- The supply of embryos comes from the surplus embryos which were not placed into a female's uterus during fertility treatment. Once the stem cells are removed these embryos are then destroyed. Some consider it unacceptable to use embryos for this purpose even if there was never any chance of the embryo being allowed to develop. Others consider that the potential benefits outweigh the ethical concerns. The human stem cells could be used to treat Parkinson's disease, Alzheimer's disease, heart disease, liver diseases, diabetes, multiple sclerosis and some cancers.
- Opponents also argue that embryonic stem cell technologies are a slippery slope to reproductive cloning and can fundamentally devalue human life. That is, there is the possibility to clone humans.

Key terms

Ethics = a set of standards that are followed by a particular group of individuals and are designed to regulate their behaviour. They determine what is acceptable.

***In vitro* fertilisation** = a technique which involves mixing a female's egg or oocyte with the partner's sperm in a dish where fertilisation takes place.

Grade boost

You must have a good knowledge of these ethical issues. Consider writing an essay entitled 'What are the arguments for and against tissue culture?' Plan your essay by making two columns and inserting the points in note form.

Pointer

50% of the treated females will eventually become pregnant, whilst almost 60% of those with no obvious cause will achieve pregnancy, even without fertility treatment, within five years.

Key terms

Meristem = growing points where cells divide rapidly by mitosis.

Totipotent (cells) = cells capable of differentiation.

>> *Pointer*

Conventional methods of plant propagation, such as taking cuttings, have been used for centuries. Using plant tissue, culture cells are taken from stock plants that have desirable characteristics and have commercial value. Micropropagation is sometimes referred to as a test-tube plant culture.

Grade boost

Not all plant cells are totipotent. Xylem and phloem are highly specialised for their particular functions.

 quickfire

⑥② Why are sterile conditions necessary in micropropagation?

quickfire

⑥③ Name the process by which totipotent cells develop into root and shoot cells.

Micropropagation (plant tissue culture)

Micropropagation involves the cloning of plants. It is an extremely cost-effective way of producing large numbers of genetically identical plants which are clones of a single parent.

The technique of micropropagation is based on the ability of differentiated plant cells to give rise to all the different cells of the adult plant. In other words, many plant cells are **totipotent**. Under the right conditions many plant cells can develop into any other cell.

At the tip of the roots and shoots of plants are areas called **meristems**. If cells are removed from the meristem and placed in suitable conditions, new, genetically identical, plants will develop.

These steps are generally followed in micropropagation:

1. A plant with the desired characteristics is selected.

2. A scalpel is used to remove the meristem from the shoot.

3. The meristem is cut into small pieces called explants.

4. The explants are placed onto a sterile, aerated nutrient medium, such as agar jelly.

5. The cells are allowed to divide by mitosis producing a mass of undifferentiated cells, called a callus.

6. The callus is subdivided and each piece is allowed to differentiate into a plantlet.

7. When they have reached a suitable size the plantlets are transplanted into sterile soil.

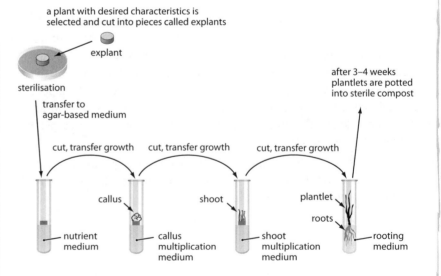

Stages in micropropagation.

The advantages of micropropagation are:

- Large numbers of plants can be grown in sterile controlled conditions ensuring a greater survival rate than would be the case if seeds were planted outside.
- Good quality stock are selected, possessing qualities such as resistance to disease or high yield.
- The crop is uniform since the plants are genetically identical. From a commercial viewpoint this is very important.
- Large numbers of plants can be stored in a small area with reduced heating and lighting costs.
- Unique genotypes can be preserved.
- Reduced space is required for transport.
- Only healthy stock are selected so plant diseases can be eliminated.

The disadvantages of micropropagation are:

- Sterile conditions have to be maintained otherwise bacterial or fungal contamination of the culture medium may result, with subsequent loss of plants.
- The plants are genetically unstable with an increased rate of mutation in medium-grown cells leading to abnormality in the plantlets. Regular inspection is needed to remove any defective individuals, thus labour costs are higher than with traditional propagation methods.

Key term

Gene probe = short piece of DNA the sequences of which are complementary to the mutated sequences.

64 State two advantages of micropropagation for large suppliers such as supermarkets.

65 What two phrases summarise the disadvantages of micropropagation?

The Human Genome Project

The main aims of the project are to:

- Determine the sequence of the four bases, A, T, G and C throughout all the human DNA.
- Identify all the genes formed by the bases.
- Find the location of the genes on the 23 human chromosomes.
- Store this information on databases.
- Consider all the ethical, social and legal issues which arise from obtaining information about the human genome.

Beneficial applications

The information enables scientists to know exactly which sections of DNA, on which chromosomes, are responsible for the many different inherited diseases. The process takes place as follows:

- A DNA sample is obtained from a patient and scanned for mutated sequences.
- **Gene probes** are used to seek their complement among the three billion base pairs of the individual's genome.
- If the mutated sequence is present, the probe will bind to it and flag the mutation.

» Pointer

The Project began in 1990 involving scientists in many countries. It has been a mammoth task determining the order of bases in the human genome as well as the identification of genes, their sequencing and mapping. The identification of the 20,000 to 25,000 genes in human DNA took 13 years to complete. The next challenge is to assign functions to the identified genes.

» Pointer

Knowing the base sequence of a normal, functioning gene makes it possible to eliminate all risk of the disease by correcting or replacing the faulty allele in humans.

»» Pointer

The incidence of some inherited diseases such as thalassaemia (an inherited blood anaemia disease common in some Mediterranean countries) is falling as a result of genetic testing.

»» Pointer

The health trend is a move to prevention rather than cure. The former is far more cost-effective in the long term as well as being beneficial to the population as a whole.

Another method of DNA testing involves comparing the sequence of DNA bases in a patient's gene to a normal version of the gene. Cost of testing can be very expensive and depends on the sizes of the genes and the numbers of mutations tested.

The following are some of the main uses of genetic testing:

- Carrier screening, which involves identifying unaffected individuals who carry one copy of a gene (recessive) for a disease that requires two copies for the disease to be expressed.
- Pre-implantation genetic diagnosis.
- Pre-natal diagnostic testing.
- Newborn baby screening.
- Pre-symptomatic testing for predicting adult-onset disorders such as Huntington's disease.
- Pre-symptomatic testing for estimating the risk of developing adult-onset cancers and Alzheimer's disease.
- Confirmation that an individual has a suspected disease.
- Forensic/identity testing.

Some applications in more detail:

- Using a sample of DNA from a person it is possible to identify whether that person is a carrier of a faulty gene such as that which causes cystic fibrosis. People who are carriers may decide not to have children or to have an antenatal genetic test to check if their child will be born with the disease.
- Some genes that have been identified play a contributory role in diseases later in life, such as Alzheimer's disease and breast cancer. Although genes play a part in disease development, so does the environment, which includes people's diet and whether they smoke, etc. Genetic testing can give an idea of the probability of developing a particular disease. Those people at greatest risk can then be targeted by health authorities, screened at regular intervals and given appropriate advice about how to reduce the risk by changing their lifestyle. Once the base sequence of a gene is known it is then possible to find the protein that it codes for. Once the structure of that protein is known it is possible to design drugs whose molecules would fit it perfectly. It may be possible to design drugs that act against the gene itself.

The pros and cons of gene testing

- Gene testing has already dramatically improved lives. Some tests are used to clarify a diagnosis and direct a physician toward appropriate treatments, while others allow families to avoid having children with devastating diseases or identify people at high risk for conditions that may be preventable.
- Commercialised gene tests for adult-onset disorders such as Alzheimer's disease and some cancers are the subject of most of the debate over gene testing. These tests are targeted to healthy (presymptomatic) people who are

identified as being at high risk because of a strong family medical history for the disorder. The tests give only a probability for developing the disorder. One of the most serious limitations of these susceptibility tests is the difficulty in interpreting a positive result, because some people who carry a disease-associated mutation never develop the disease. Scientists believe that these mutations may work together with other unknown mutations or with environmental factors to cause disease.

- A limitation of all medical testing is the possibility for laboratory errors. These might be due to sample misidentification, contamination of the chemicals used for testing, or other factors.

- Many in the medical establishment feel that uncertainties surrounding test interpretation, the current lack of available medical options for these diseases, the tests' potential for provoking anxiety, and risks for discrimination and social stigmatisation could outweigh the benefits of testing.

- There are also a number of social concerns:
  - Who should have access to personal genetic information and how will it be used?
  - Who owns and controls the genetic information?
  - Should parents have the right to have their children tested for adult-onset diseases?
  - Is there a danger of one day producing human clones?

>> **Pointer**

There are many diseases that are caused by faulty alleles of genes. The aim of gene therapy is to treat a genetic disease by replacing defective genes in the patient's body with copies of a new DNA sequence. About 60% of currently approved gene therapy procedures are targeting cancer with about 25% aiming to treat genetic disorders such as cystic fibrosis.

Gene therapy

The main problem with gene therapy lies in developing a gene delivery system, that is, a means of inserting 'normal' versions of genes into a person's cells and ensuring that they function correctly once they get there.

Gene therapy usually requires a vector or carrier to introduce the DNA. The majority of procedures use viruses as vectors to deliver the selected gene to the target cells. Some use liposomes and others use injection of naked plasma DNA.

There are two possible ways of replacing defective genes:

- Gene therapy involving somatic cell therapy targets cells in the affected tissues. This method may be therapeutic, but the genetic changes are not inherited.

- Germ-line therapy, involves the introduction of corrective genes into germ-line cells, that is, the gene is replaced in the egg and will enable genetic corrections to be inherited.

>> **Pointer**

The use of stem cells, rather than mature somatic cells, is longer lasting in patients.

>> **Pointer**

Inserting a functional gene does not remove the defective gene. Cells produce both functional and non-functional proteins at the same time.

Key term

Liposome = minute spheres of lipid molecules.

>> *Pointer*

Trials have begun using this novel technique. The treatment does not solve the digestive problems of the patient but has the potential to solve the problem of congested and infected lungs.

>> *Pointer*

The advantages of gene therapy far outweigh the disadvantages. To give a child that would be born with a genetic disease the chance of a normal life, or to prevent the development of cancer in an individual are goals that medical science must aspire to.

quickfire

66 What events must take place once the replacement gene is inside the lung cell for the treatment to be successful?

Cystic fibrosis

Cystic fibrosis is due to a defective autosomal recessive allele. In the UK one person in 2000 suffers from the condition. Sufferers produce a thick sticky mucus from the epithelial cells lining certain passageways in the body. These secretions lead to a number of problems:

- The pancreatic duct becomes blocked, preventing pancreatic enzymes from reaching the duodenum and so food digestion is incomplete.
- The bronchioles and alveoli of the lungs become clogged, causing congestion and difficulty in breathing. The mucus is difficult to remove and leads to recurrent infections.

To relieve the distress with breathing, frequent daily chest physiotherapy massage is needed to keep the airways open. The sufferer also has impaired digestion and a limited absorption of food. Children with the condition have large appetites to try to compensate.

To inherit the disease both parents must be carriers of the defective recessive allele. Carriers can be identified using a simple blood test. The normal gene codes for the production of a protein found in the cell membrane. This protein, called cystic fibrosis transmembrane regulator (CFTR), transports chloride ions out of cells into mucus. Sodium ions follow out of the cells and water passes out of the cell by osmosis. This makes the mucus that lines the air passages a watery consistency. The protein of cystic fibrosis sufferers lacks just one amino acid and so cannot perform its transport function.

Microbiologists have succeeded in isolating and cloning the gene which codes for the CFTR protein.

The gene therapy technique works as follows:

- The genes are inserted into **liposomes**. This involves wrapping the gene in lipid molecules that can pass through the membranes of lung epithelial cells.
- An aerosol inhaler is used to add the non-defective gene to the epithelial cells of the lung.
- The liposomes fuse with the phospholipid bilayer of the cell membrane and the DNA enters the cells. These cells start to express the inserted gene by making the protein CFTR.

Genetic counselling

If a family has a history of a genetic defect, unaffected members can consult a genetic counsellor for advice on the risk of bearing an affected child. Advice may be based on:

- Whether there is a history of the disorder in the family.
- Whether the parents are closely related.
- The frequency of the faulty gene in the general population.

Genetic screening

Once it is established that there is a risk of passing on a defective gene, there are means of investigating whether a child is affected before it is born. On the basis of these tests the parents can decide whether or not to have the pregnancy terminated. Techniques involved include:

- A blood test – there is a simple blood test for detecting cystic fibrosis.
- Amniocentesis – this involves withdrawing some of the amniotic fluid during the early stages of pregnancy. The fluid contains cells that have floated away from the surface of the embryo. These cells may be analysed microscopically.
- Chorionic villus sampling – early in pregnancy (within 8–10 weeks) tiny samples of foetal tissue are withdrawn from the uterus and cells are cultured and examined under the microscope.

Advantages and disadvantages of gene therapy

Genetic screening produces much controversy and raises many ethical and legal issues. Many believe that this involves an invasion of privacy. Some also believe that if prenatal tests are carried out, finding defective genes will lead to an increase in the number of abortions. Individuals with defects may be placed in a high risk group for insurance purposes to cover the cost of treatment. This would mean that insurance cover would be very expensive or even impossible to obtain.

Couples may find that they are carriers of a genetic disease and must decide if they want to have a child that could be born with a defect.

Another problem involves the regulation of gene therapy in its use solely for reducing defects. Many fear that companies will use gene therapy for the wrong reasons, such as choosing or modifying the characteristics of a child.

Genetic engineering

Applications of genetic engineering include the transfer of:

- Genes into bacteria, so that they can make useful products such as insulin.
- Genes into plants and animals so that they acquire new characteristics, for example resistance to disease.
- Genes into humans so that they no longer suffer from genetic diseases such as cystic fibrosis.

The process of producing a protein using the DNA technology of gene transfer and cloning involves the following stages:

- Isolation of the DNA fragments.
- Insertion of the DNA fragment into a vector.
- The transfer of DNA into suitable host cells.
- Identification of the host cells that have taken up the gene by use of gene markers.
- Growth of the host cells.

Key terms (page 100)

Clone = a population of genetically identical cells or organisms.

DNA ligases = enzymes which join together portions of DNA.

Donor DNA = a gene that is isolated for insertion.

Plasmids = circular loops of DNA found in bacteria. The plasmid is known as a vector.

Recombinant DNA = DNA which results from the combination of fragments from two different organisms.

Restriction enzymes = enzymes which cut DNA molecules between specific base sequences.

Sticky ends = the two ends of the 'foreign' DNA segment. They have a short row of unpaired bases that match the complementary bases at the two ends of the opened-up plasmid.

Grade boost

The same restriction enzyme is used to cut open the donor DNA and the plasmid to ensure that the sticky ends are complementary. When mixed the DNA fragments may then become incorporated into the plasmids.

quickfire

67 The bacterium, *E.coli* is widely distributed and capable of exchanging genetic material with other types of bacteria. Suggest why some scientists consider that the use of recombinant DNA could be dangerous.

≫ *Pointer*

The technique is based on the knowledge that some plasmids carry a gene for antibiotic resistance and this is unaffected by the introduction of the new gene.

To explain the principles of using gene technology to produce useful molecules on a large scale, the production of insulin is described, using bacteria called *E.coli*.

Isolating the gene from a **donor DNA** molecule

The gene coding for insulin is located using a gene probe and then isolated from the rest of the DNA in a human cell. An enzyme called restriction endonuclease is used to cut the DNA into small pieces allowing individual genes to be isolated. The enzyme cuts DNA between specific base sequences which the enzyme recognises. Most **restriction enzymes** split the two strands in a staggered sequence. The unpaired bases at the cut form **sticky ends**.

Inserting the gene into a vector

To get the gene into a bacterium a go-between or vector is used. The vector, in this instance, is a **plasmid**, a small, circular piece of DNA found in bacteria. To obtain the plasmids, the bacteria containing them are treated to dissolve their cell walls and the plasmids are separated from the cell debris. The circular DNA molecule making up the plasmid is cut open using the same enzyme, restriction endonuclease. The enzyme makes staggered cuts, called 'sticky ends', which allow the donor DNA to be spliced into the vector DNA. This takes place when the donor and vector DNA are mixed together. The sticky ends are complementary and the C and G bases on their sticky ends pair up. Another group of enzymes, called **DNA ligases**, are used to join the donor and vector DNA together.

This created DNA is called **recombinant DNA**.

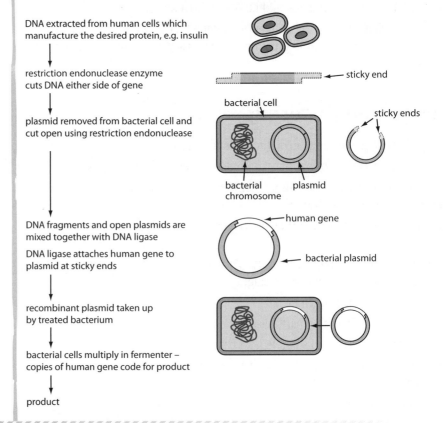

DNA extracted from human cells which manufacture the desired protein, e.g. insulin

↓

restriction endonuclease enzyme cuts DNA either side of gene

↓

plasmid removed from bacterial cell and cut open using restriction endonuclease

↓

DNA fragments and open plasmids are mixed together with DNA ligase

DNA ligase attaches human gene to plasmid at sticky ends

↓

recombinant plasmid taken up by treated bacterium

↓

bacterial cells multiply in fermenter – copies of human gene code for product

↓

product

sticky end

bacterial cell

sticky ends

bacterial chromosome   plasmid

human gene

bacterial plasmid

Manufacture

Using the bacteria that have taken up a piece of foreign DNA successfully, the foreign DNA replicates along with the rest of the plasmid every time the bacterial cell divides. **Cloning** of the recombinant containing bacteria results in the production of multiple copies of the recombinant gene. That is, the bacteria divide repeatedly and give rise to a large population of bacterial cells all of which contain replicas of the foreign DNA.

The genetically modified bacteria are cultured on a large scale using a fermenter and produce insulin which is extracted and purified. Thus, human insulin can be used instead of extracting insulin from animals. Also large quantities of product are produced quickly and relatively cheaply.

Marker genes can be used in two ways:

- To indicate that new genes have been incorporated into host cells. Some may be radioactive so that the position of the labelled gene can be easily located.

- To identify bacterial cells containing genetically engineered plasmids using marker genes that confer antibiotic resistance.

When the bacteria and plasmids are mixed together, only a small proportion of the bacteria (as few as 1%) take up the plasmids. All the bacterial cells are grown on a medium that contains the antibiotic, ampicillin. Bacterial cells that have taken up the plasmids will have acquired the gene for ampicillin resistance. These bacterial cells are able to break down the antibiotic and survive.

Using reverse transcriptase

Locating the correct piece of DNA is not easy, as the cell contains two copies only of the DNA. However, the cell may contain large numbers of molecules of mRNA that has been transcribed from it. This is especially true if cells can be used which are known to synthesise and secrete the required product. The functional mRNA coding for insulin will be present in large quantities in the cytoplasm of the pancreas.

- This mRNA can be extracted.

- The addition of an enzyme, **reverse transcriptase**, made from a group of viruses called retroviruses, is used to make a DNA copy of the mRNA. This single strand of DNA is called copy DNA or cDNA. Many copies of cDNA are made.

- The addition of DNA polymerase converts this to a double strand for insertion into a plasmid as described on page 100.

Key term

Reverse transcriptase = enzymes used to synthesise DNA from mRNA in specific cells.

 **quickfire**

⑥⑧ Suggest one advantage of the reverse transcriptase technique over the method described on page 100.

 **quickfire**

⑥⑨ Why are gene markers necessary?

》 *Pointer*

The low take-up may be explained as some plasmids close up without incorporating the DNA fragment.

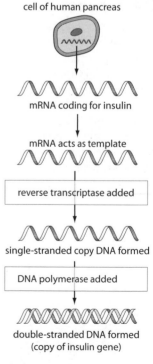

cell of human pancreas

↓

mRNA coding for insulin

↓

mRNA acts as template

reverse transcriptase added

↓

single-stranded copy DNA formed

DNA polymerase added

↓

double-stranded DNA formed
(copy of insulin gene)

Making copy DNA.

Key term

Transgenic = an organism that has had its genotype altered, producing a new strain of organism. Also known as genetically modified organisms.

Grade boost

Bacteria are readily introduced into plants. Certain species naturally attack damaged plants and cause the plant cells to multiply and form a tumour. The bacteria do this by inserting genes from their own plasmids into one of the plant's chromosomes. The plasmid gene links with the DNA of the plant but stimulates the growth of a tumour. Scientists can replace the tumour-forming genes in the bacterial plasmids with useful genes.

Grade boost

Questions are often asked regarding GM foods.

Are there potential risks in producing GM crops?

Will the products and ingredients made from GM crops be labelled?

Will the nutritional properties be affected?

Will the environment be affected?

Genetically modified organisms

Transgenic plants

The following are examples of GM crops:

- Soya beans. In many countries soya beans are very important as a source of food. They are used as an ingredient in a wide range of foods such as flour, protein and oil. About 60% of food products such as bread, biscuits, baby foods, soya milk, etc., are soya based. Certain varieties of soya plants have been modified to be tolerant to a weed-killer. This allows the weed-killer to be sprayed onto the crop without affecting it but kills all the weeds. The weed-killer breaks down in the soil into harmless components.

- Tomatoes. Tomatoes ripen naturally as they produce an enzyme which breaks down the pectin in their cell walls. Tomatoes sold at the supermarket need to be firm and at their best when displayed. This creates a problem for supermarkets that need to transport tomatoes long distances from their supplier. Scientists have developed a genetically modified tomato called 'Flavr Savr'. A gene has been introduced into the tomato plant having a base sequence complementary to that of the gene producing the enzyme. The mRNA transcribed from this inserted gene is therefore complementary to the mRNA stand of the original gene. The two combine to form a double strand. This prevents the mRNA of the original gene from being translated and effectively blocks the production of the enzyme. The result is that Flavr Savr tomatoes have a longer shelf life and a better taste.

Benefits and concerns

On a world-wide scale GM crops have tremendous potential value:

- Solving food shortages in various parts of the world; perhaps also enabling crops to be grown in drought areas.
- Producing improved food with improved flavour and better keeping qualities.
- Reducing the harmful effects of modern farming by introducing nitrogen-fixing genes into crops such as rice and wheat, reducing the use of artificial fertilisers.
- Introducing genes that confer resistance to insects, weeds and diseases.
- Real benefits from improved animal production might be seen in the Third World. For example, it may one day be possible to introduce disease resistance into otherwise vulnerable animals. The Bovine Genome Project could result in, for instance, resistance to trypanosomiasis being introduced into more productive breeds of cattle from their naturally resistant African counterparts.

People are opposed to GM crops for the following reasons:

- There are concerns that the GM plants through pollination will transfer their genes to wild relatives or similar crops growing nearby with unforeseen effects. For example, plants with introduced genes that enable them to resist insect attack will quickly lead to the establishment of a resistant population of insect pests. Long-term field trials will establish whether these concerns are well founded.

- GM crops contain marker genes. Some marker genes confer antibiotic resistance. There is concern that these genes may be transferred to the bacteria in the intestine of the consumer.

- Plant breeding may fall into the hands of just a few commercial companies and the varieties they offer to the farmer will be reduced. This could make crops more susceptible to attack by pests and diseases and lead to a reduction in the use of important old varieties of their wild relatives.

- If GM crops are to be grown commercially in the UK, organic farm produce will be compromised. Pollen from GM crops, spread on the wind and by insects, could find its way into organic fields and beehives.

Genetic fingerprinting

About 90% of the DNA of the human chromosome has no known function. Individuals acquire different sequences of this non-functional DNA. They vary in length but consist of sequences of bases, 20–40 bases long, often repeated many times. These unique lengths of non-coding DNA, known as hyper-variable regions (HVR) or short tandem repeats (STRs), are passed on to the offspring. It is the number of times that these lengths of non-coding DNA are repeated that is used to show the differences between individuals.

1. The DNA is extracted from the sample and cut into small fragments using restriction endonucleases.

2. The DNA fragments are separated by a technique known as **electrophoresis**. Since the fragments are negatively charged, they move towards the positive terminal. The smaller the fragment, the faster it moves and the DNA becomes separated into bands according to the size of the fragments.

3. The trough is covered with a nylon membrane and the fragments are transferred to the membrane by a process called Southern blotting.

4. Radioactive DNA probes (now largely replaced by non-radioactive or chemi-luminescent probes) are used to attach to specific parts of the fragments and any unbound fragments are washed off.

5. The nylon membrane with DNA fragments attached is placed under X-ray film and the radioactive probes expose the film.

6. This autoradiograph reveals a pattern of light and dark bands (the dark band indicates where a radioactive probe is present) which are unique to individuals and is called a genetic fingerprint.

Key term

Electrophoresis = exposing the fragments of DNA to an electric current in a trough of gel.

≫ Pointer

Since the introduction of GM crops at the end of the 20th century, there has been an increase in public concern and some scepticism regarding the research carried out by government agencies. As a result many retailers have banned GM ingredients from their own brand products. This will remain until public confidence in the long-term use of GM crops is restored.

quickfire

⑦⓪ What is the main concern regarding the pollen of GM crops?

≫ Pointer

A person's DNA profile is known as their 'genetic fingerprint'. An individual's genetic fingerprint is unique. The technique can be used to provide forensic evidence and also determine parents in paternity cases. Since body cells contain the same DNA, tissues such as blood, hair, skin cells or semen can be used.

quickfire

⑦① Name the enzyme used to cut the DNA.

The bands in a fingerprint are inherited from both parents: these can be used in paternity suits and can also be used to convict criminals. To do this, white blood cells are taken from the mother and the possible father. The bands of the mother are subtracted from the child's pattern. If the man is the true father, he must possess all the remaining bands in the child's genetic fingerprint.

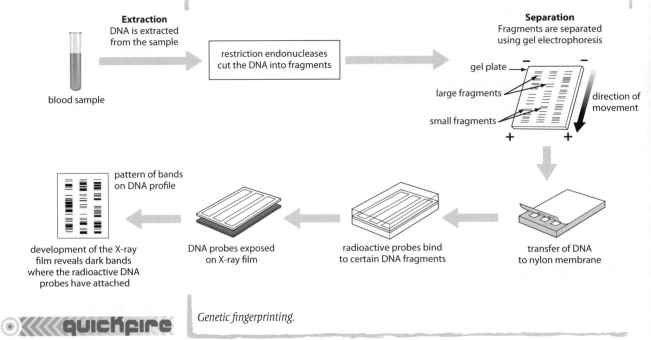

Extraction
DNA is extracted from the sample

blood sample

restriction endonucleases cut the DNA into fragments

Separation
Fragments are separated using gel electrophoresis

gel plate
large fragments
small fragments
direction of movement

pattern of bands on DNA profile

development of the X-ray film reveals dark bands where the radioactive DNA probes have attached

DNA probes exposed on X-ray film

radioactive probes bind to certain DNA fragments

transfer of DNA to nylon membrane

Genetic fingerprinting.

quickfire

⑦② When DNA strands are separated in the PCR, what type of bond is broken?

Grade boost

Candidates often fail to appreciate the importance of the temperature changes in the PCR.

quickfire

⑦③ Why is it important that the fragments of DNA used in PCR are not contaminated with any other biological material?

quickfire

⑦④ Explain why forensic scientists often use PCR when producing a genetic fingerprint.

Polymerase chain reaction

PCR is really semi-conservative replication of DNA in a test-tube. The sample of DNA is dissolved in a buffer and mixed with the enzyme, DNA polymerase, nucleotides and short pieces of DNA called primers, which act as signals to the DNA polymerase to start copying.

The stages in the process are as follows:

1. The original DNA (target DNA) is denatured by heating to 95°C and it separates into two single strands.

2. The solution is cooled to 55°C triggering the primers to join to the complementary base sequences on each of the single strands of DNA. This in turn triggers DNA replication.

3. The solution is heated to 70°C and DNA polymerase (which is not denatured at this temperature) catalyses the synthesis of a complementary strand for each of the single strands of DNA, producing two identical double strands of DNA.

4. Steps 1–3 are repeated many times, doubling the quantity of DNA produced each time.

Issues of privacy

Scientists are confronted with vast quantities of data, a large proportion of which is genetic fingerprinting information. This information is used for phylogenetic studies, forensic science, paternity studies, etc. This raises concerns regarding the storage of this information as well as who has access to the data. Will insurance companies use the data to determine life and health insurance premiums?

On the wider issue of biodiversity of human beings, efforts are being made to store genetic material from the many races and tribes of the world before isolated tribes are intermixed and lost. This is scientifically useful, but careful ethical standards need to be maintained in order that genetic privacy is maintained and that no misuse of the information occurs in the future.

The advantages and disadvantages of genetic engineering

There are numerous advantages:

- The large-scale production of complex proteins or peptides that cannot be made by other methods.
- The production of higher yielding crops with superior keeping qualities, etc.
- The health benefits for treating genetic diseases.

However, there are concerns that the development of genetic engineering will introduce the possibilities of misuse:

- Germ-line gene therapy is controversial as it involves replacing the defective gene or allele with healthy genes inside the fertilised egg. Some genes have no apparent function other than to control or 'switch off' other genes on the same chromosome. Tampering with genes in the fertilised egg could result in unforeseen effects in future generations.
- There are a number of potential hazards associated with genetic engineering and it is impossible to predict what the consequences might be of releasing genetically engineered organisms into the environment. The potential hazards are:
  - A new gene, on insertion, may disrupt normal gene function. For example, a potentially dangerous micro-organism with a new gene may become a dangerous pathogen if it is released into the environment.
  - Bacteria readily exchange genetic material. The recombinant DNA might get into other organisms. For example, herbicide resistance might be transferred to a weed species.
  - The deliberate use of antibiotic resistant genes in *E. coli*, which lives in the human gut, and the possibility that these genes could be accidentally transferred to human pathogens.
  - The possibility of transfer of DNA with linked pathogenic genes, for example oncogenes increasing cancer risks.

>> *Pointer*

There are economic issues associated with the new techniques which are technically complicated and therefore very expensive on an industrial scale.

Grade boost

The main ethical question is whether scientists have the right to alter the genotype of future generations. Do scientists know enough about how genes interact with each other?

75 What is meant by 'germ line therapy'?

>> *Pointer*

Despite legislation restricting the production and field testing of transgenic plants and animals, there remain reservations about the long-term effects of the manipulation of the human genome and the production of GM modified organisms.

Energy and ecosystems

Energy flow

Key terms

Community = the different populations of species that live in a habitat.

Decomposers = microbes, bacteria and fungi that obtain nutrients from dead organisms and faeces. They complete the process of decomposition started by detritivores.

Detritivores = organisms such as earthworms which feed on small fragments of organic debris, called detritus, made up of non-living organic material, such as faeces, fallen leaves and the remains of dead organisms.

Ecosystem = a natural unit of living (biotic) components in a given area, as well as the non-living (abiotic) factors with which they interact.

Habitat = the particular area occupied by a population. That is, the place where an organism lives. It has biotic and abiotic features which separate it from other habitats.

Energy flow through the ecosystem

The study of the flow of energy through the **ecosystem** is known as ecological energetics.

The following summarises the flow of energy through the ecosystem:

- Green plants are called producers and trap solar energy and manufacture sugars from simple raw materials by the process of photosynthesis.
- The sun's energy is passed from one feeding or trophic level to another through the ecosystem.
- Herbivores (primary consumers) are animals that feed on plants. Carnivores are animals that feed on other animals.
- Each of these groups forms a feeding or trophic level with energy passing from each level to a higher one as material is eaten.
- Eventually the energy leaves the system as heat.
- Only a small amount of the total energy that reaches the plant as light is incorporated into plant tissues. As energy is passed along the food chain there is a large loss at each level.
- At each level energy is lost through respiration, and through the excretion of waste products, so the amount of energy is reduced.
- The sequence from plant to herbivore to carnivore is a food chain and is the route by which energy passes between trophic levels.
- It is the loss of energy at each level which limits the length of a food chain, so the number of links in a chain is normally limited to four or five.
- On the death of producers and consumers, some energy remains locked up in the organic compounds of which they are made. **Detritivores** and **decomposers** feed as saprobionts and contribute to the recycling of nutrients.

Energy flow though producers

- The energy flowing from one organism to another in the food chain originates as sunlight.
- A large proportion of the energy that falls on a plant is not absorbed.
- If it is assumed that 100 units of energy per unit time reach the leaves of a crop plant, the diagram on page 107 shows what happens to the energy.

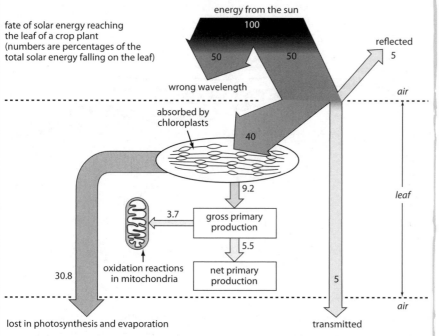

fate of solar energy reaching the leaf of a crop plant (numbers are percentages of the total solar energy falling on the leaf)

Energy loss in plants.

Pointer

Biological productivity has two components:
Primary productivity – the production of new organic matter by green plants.
Secondary productivity – the production of new organic matter by consumers.

Grade boost

Be prepared to carry out calculations in exam questions.

- Gross primary productivity (GPP) is the rate at which products, such as glucose, are formed. A substantial amount of gross production is used up in respiration by the plant.

GPP – respiration = net production.

- That which is left over after respiration is called net primary productivity (NPP). This represents the food available to primary consumers.

- Secondary productivity is the rate at which consumers accumulate energy in the form of cells or tissues.

Energy flow through consumers

Herbivores are not able to eat all the vegetation available to them.

Consider a cow feeding on grass in a field:

- Some of the plant material is not eaten by the cow. Cattle grazing a field will eat the grasses and edible weeds but do not eat the roots and often leave the woody parts of the plants.

- Cows feed on plant material that contains cellulose, which they are unable to digest. This passes out of the body as faeces containing a high proportion of undigested matter. (In terms of the ecosystem this energy is not wasted as it is available to decomposers.)

- Some of the food material in the field is being eaten by other herbivores such as rabbits.

Grade boost

Consumers have a conversion efficiency of about 10%, that is, for every 100 grams of plant material taken in or ingested, only about 10 grams is incorporated into herbivore biomass. This means that only part of the NPP of the ecosystem is transferred to the primary consumers.

Key terms

Biomass = the mass of living material present at a given time.

Climax community = a community that has reached equilibrium with its environment and no further change occurs.

Succession = the change in structure and composition of species of a community over time.

76 Why do carnivores have a much higher secondary productivity than herbivores?

≫ Pointer

Carnivores absorb almost twice as much energy per unit mass of food compared with herbivores.

≫ Pointer

In practice obtaining the data to construct an energy pyramid is difficult as it involves incineration of living material.

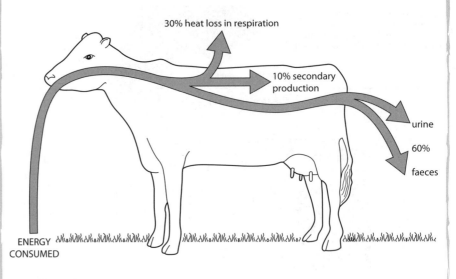

Energy flow through cow.

Herbivores have a lower secondary productivity than carnivores. That is, carnivores are more efficient at energy conversion than herbivores. They have a much higher secondary productivity. This is because their protein-rich diet is more readily and efficiently digested. Only about 20% of the energy intake is lost in the faeces and urine of carnivores compared with a loss of about 60% in herbivores.

Pyramids of energy

- The number of organisms, their **biomass** or the amount of energy contained in each trophic level, can be represented in diagrams with a bar for each level. These are known as pyramids. However, the most accurate way of representing feeding relationships in a community is to use a pyramid of energy, which provides a quantitative account of the feeding relationships in a community.

- A pyramid of energy shows the quantity of energy transferred from one trophic level to the next, per unit area or volume, per unit time. This represents the total energy requirement of each successive trophic level in a food chain.

- As material passes up through the food chain, energy is lost in respiration as heat, and in excretion, so the size of the bars decreases sharply. Since only some of the energy is passed on from one level to the next, energy pyramids are never inverted as in biomass pyramids.

- Pyramids of energy enable ease of comparison of the efficiency of energy transfer to be made from one trophic level to the next between different communities.

Community and succession

The distribution of species does not necessarily remain the same over long periods of time. Ecosystems are dynamic and subject to change. Organisms and their environment interact, if one changes so does the other. A change in the environment affects the organisms, and a change in the organisms affects the environment.

- Primary **succession** refers to the introduction of plants/animals into areas that have not previously supported a community, for example bare rock, or the site of volcanic eruption.
- Secondary succession refers to the reintroduction of organisms into a bare habitat previously occupied by plants and animals. If the original vegetation is removed, for example by fire, or by tree felling, the area rapidly becomes re-colonised by a succession of different plants and animals.

In any area, over time, new organisms replace existing ones, that is, species diversity increases until a stable state is reached. All successions usually involve changes in community structure and function until a community reaches a climax of succession known as the **climax community**, for example a mature woodland.

Consider the colonisation of bare rock.

The first organisms to colonise the bare rock are algae and lichens. These plants are called pioneer species and form a pioneer community. Lichens slowly erode the rock. This together with the weathering of the rock and the accumulation of dead and decomposing organic material leads to the formation of a primitive soil. Wind-blown spores allow mosses to appear and, as the soil develops, grasses become established. As the soil builds up, deep-rooted shrubs appear. Over a very long time trees such as oak become established. This is then known as the climax community. This is a stable condition dominated by long-lived plants.

In a secondary succession, seeds, spores and organs of vegetative reproduction may remain in the soil and dispersal of plants and migration of animals will assist in colonisation of the habitat.

Human interference can affect a succession and may prevent the natural development of the climax community:

- Grazing by sheep.
- Heather moorland management by controlled burning for grouse shooting.
- Farming of land.
- Deforestation and soil erosion.

 Pointer

It should be realised that a community consists of animals as well as plants and that the animals have undergone a similar succession dictated by the plant types present at each stage.

quickfire

(77) What is the main difference between primary and secondary succession?

quickfire

(78) Name the plant type found in a climax community.

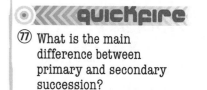
bare rock
colonised by algae,
fungi and lichens

pioneer community
of heather and mosses

herbs and low-growing shrubs

taller shrubs

birch and pine saplings

oak/beech forest

Succession.

Effects of human activities

Human influences on the environment have created new selection pressures.

Resistance

Key term

Resistance = the ability of an organism to survive exposure to a dose of that poison which would normally be lethal to it.

Warfarin resistance in rats

A dominant allele R at a single locus in rats confers **resistance**. However, this allele also confers a requirement for vitamin K:

- Heterozygotes (Rr) are resistant to warfarin and have only a small requirement for vitamin K.
- Homozygotes (RR) are resistant to warfarin but have a massive requirement for vitamin K which is difficult to meet.
- Homozygotes (rr) are killed by warfarin but have a much better chance of survival than RR rats if warfarin is absent from the environment.

This is an example of heterozygote advantage where the heterozygotes are favoured by selection and both alleles Rr will be maintained in the population with all three genotypes RR, Rr and rr being produced in each generation. In the rat population both warfarin sensitive and warfarin resistant alleles are maintained in areas where warfarin is used as a selective agent.

> **Pointer**
>
> The pesticide 'warfarin', which is an anticoagulant, has been used on a large scale to control the rat (*Rattus norvegicus*) population. Rats have become resistant to warfarin.

> **Pointer**
>
> MRSA (methicillin-resistant *Staphylococcus aureus*) has developed a resistance to several antibiotics.

Antibiotic resistance

In agriculture many farm animals are reared indoors so that they grow more rapidly. In these crowded conditions there is a greater risk of disease spreading; therefore broad-spectrum antibiotics are often added to animal food in an attempt to prevent disease.

Many bacteria that were previously susceptible to antibiotics have now become **resistant**. This resistance has arisen by mutations occurring randomly within populations of bacteria which then confer an advantage in the presence of that antibiotic. This may be the ability to produce an enzyme which breaks down the antibiotic. For example, some bacteria produce an enzyme, penicillinase, which renders penicillin ineffective. In the presence of penicillin, non-resistant forms are destroyed. There is a selection pressure favouring the resistant types. The greater the quantity and frequency of penicillin use, the greater the selection pressure.

Repeated exposure to antibiotics has led to more bacteria surviving and passing on resistant genes.

The problem has been made worse by the discovery that resistance can be transmitted between individuals of the same species. There is evidence that the resistance may be passed from one organism to another on plasmids, during conjugation (sexual reproduction). This means that a disease-causing organism can become resistant to a given antibiotic even before the antibiotic is used against them.

Grade boost

Refer back to mutations on page 80.

quickfire

(79) How are some bacteria resistant to penicillin?

Grade boost

Candidates often incorrectly state that bacteria are immune to antibiotics. They become resistant to antibiotics.

Artificial selection

Humans choose organisms showing desirable characters and breed only from these. In terms of genetics, humans rather than the environment determine which alleles are passed on to future generations and which are lost. This process of artificial selection mimics natural selection and provides evidence that selection can lead to the development of characteristics and the production of very distinct forms of organisms, as seen in many domestic animals and plant species.

Artificial selection:

- Is carried out by humans to obtain plants or animals with the characteristics humans require.
- May take many years to develop organisms with the required characteristics.
- Produces organisms belonging to the same species, which are often described as different breeds or varieties.

There are two basic methods of artificial selection:

- Inbreeding – occurs when the gametes of close relatives fuse. The problem with inbreeding is that it promotes homozygosity. That is, it increases the chance of a harmful recessive gene expressing itself, since there is a greater risk of a double recessive individual occurring. For example, plant species inbred over many generations show a degree of loss of vigour, size and fertility. This is called inbreeding depression. At intervals it is necessary to introduce new genes by outbreeding.

- Outbreeding – occurs by the crossing of unrelated varieties. Outbreeding promotes heterozygosity. It introduces hybrid vigour where the organisms sometimes grow more strongly. It arises when the new sets of chromosomes are complementary in their effects. Occasionally crosses have occurred between plants of different species, e.g. the development of modern wheat.

Here is an example of a breeding programme – milk yield in cattle. To develop cows with an increased milk yield the following steps would be carried out:

1. Test the milk yield of selected high milk yielding cows.
2. Select the cow with the highest milk yield (A).
3. Select a bull descended from a cow with a high milk yield (B).
4. Cross cow A and bull B, and select female calves.
5. Wait for these calves to mature, then test their milk yield.
6. Select the cow with the highest milk yield (C), then repeat these steps over several generations.

>> *Pointer*

Artificial selection or selective breeding of animals and plants makes use of variations that occur within a population.

⑧⓪ In genetic terms what is the main disadvantage of inbreeding?

Key term
Species conservation = the planned preservation of wildlife.

>> *Pointer*

Human activities are altering ecosystems upon which they and other species depend. In the oceans, stocks of many fishes are being depleted by over-harvesting, and some of the most productive and diverse areas, such as coral reefs and estuaries are being severely stressed.

Grade boost

The conservation of species ensures the conservation of existing gene pools.
For ethical reasons it is important to conserve potentially useful genes for future generations of humans as well as for the survival of the species itself.

◎ <<<< **quickfire**

⑧1 State three main reasons for the decline in numbers, of large mammals such as gorillas and tigers.

Human influence on biodiversity

Extinction

Extinction is a natural process that has been taking place since life first evolved. It is the current *rate* of extinction that underlies the biodiversity crisis. Scientists believe that the normal 'background' rate of extinction is one out of every million species per year. It is now estimated that human activity in tropical areas alone has increased extinction rates between 1000 and 10,000 times! Massive destruction of habitats throughout the world has been brought about by agriculture, urban development, forestry, mining, and environmental pollution. Marine life has also been affected. About one third of the planet's marine fish species rely on coral reefs. At the current rate of destruction about half of the reefs could be lost in the next 20 years.

Endangered species

The vast majority of Earth's earlier occupants, including the large and once dominant dinosaurs and tree ferns, have become extinct largely as a result of climatic, geological and biotic changes. At the present time, human activity has taken over as the main cause of species extinction. Many of the larger mammals such as mountain gorillas, giant pandas, tigers and polar bears are threatened. Their decline in numbers has three main causes:

- Loss of habitat.
- Over-hunting by humans.
- Competition from introduced species.

Other species are also threatened by additional causes such as:

- Deforestation.
- Pollution.
- Drainage of wetlands.

It is now recognised that each species may represent an important human asset, a potential source of food, useful chemicals, or disease-resistant genes. There is therefore a need for **species conservation**.

Present-day plants and animals used in agriculture and horticulture have been developed from plants and animals that were originally in the wild. Breeding increases genetic uniformity with the loss of rarer alleles. In the past breeders may have neglected some important qualities, such as resistance to cold and disease, etc. These need to be added back into highly cultivated varieties, using the wild plants and animals as a gene bank. If habitats and the wildlife that live in them are threatened, this may no longer be possible. There is also concern about the progressive destruction of the tropical rain forests.

Among the many trees and shrubs are some with medicinal properties. The extinction of any plant species before its chemical properties have been investigated could amount to an incalculable loss. In recent years there has been much concern about the loss of gene pools, and legislation has endeavoured to prevent the extinction of endangered species.

The following are some of the steps that have been taken:

- Stocks of seeds of 'traditional' varieties of plants are stored in seed banks.
- The establishment of sperm banks.
- The founding of rare breeds societies to maintain old, less commercial varieties of animals.
- The protection and breeding of endangered species in specialised zoos.
- Reintroduction programmes, e.g. Red Kite in Mid Wales.
- Global organisations, such as the World-Wide Fund for Nature, mount continuing campaigns to promote public awareness.
- International co-operation restricting trade, e.g. in ivory and whaling.
- In the UK, the Countryside Commission is the government body that promotes nature conservation. It gives advice to government and to all groups whose activities affect wildlife and their habitats:
  - It produces a range of publications.
  - It proposes schemes of management for each of the major ecosystem types, endeavouring to conserve species diversity.
  - It establishes nature reserves managed by wardens.

Education and legislation have also played their part in conservation.

Legislation has been introduced to protect endangered species and to prevent over-grazing, over-fishing, hunting of game, collection of birds' eggs, picking of wild flowers, and plant collecting.

Ecotourism is a recent method introduced to promote conservation. The aims of **ecotourism** are:

- Minimize the negative impacts of tourism.
- Contribute to conservation efforts.
- Employ local people and give money back to the community.
- Educate visitors about the local environment and culture.
- Co-operate with local people to manage natural areas.
- Provide a positive experience for both visitor and host.

Key term

Ecotourism = the responsible travel to natural areas that conserves the environment and improves the well-being of local people.

Grade boost

Consider an essay entitled: 'What are endangered species? Discuss the reasons why some species have become endangered. Discuss ways in which species be conserved for future generations.'

Key term

Monoculture = the simultaneous growth of large numbers of crop plants of similar age and type within a defined area.

>> *Pointer*

The increase in human population has meant that more food has to be produced to support it. In agriculture an increase in land use and overfishing of the oceans has led to a conflict between production and conservation. The use of pesticides and fertilisers has improved crop yield but environmental issues arise from their use.

quickfire

⑧② Why does yield progressively decline if the same crops are grown in the same field year after year?

>> *Pointer*

Forests cover about 34% of the world's land surface. However, about half the world's forests have been cut down by deforestation during the last 30 years.

Agricultural exploitation

Both the efficiency and the intensity of food production are being continually increased to meet the demands to produce more food for human consumption.

Following World War II more land was cultivated, the use of fertilisers and pesticides was increased, mechanisation was introduced. These changes had a number of environmental implications:

- To make larger fields to enable machinery that was needed to prepare the soil and harvest crops, many hedgerows were removed.
- In the larger fields, single crops were grown, for example wheat and barley. This **monoculture** leads to reduced species diversity. Also, if the same crop is grown on the same plot year after year, yield progressively declines. This is due to two main factors:
  - Mineral depletion – intensive cultivation necessitated a huge increase in the use of inorganic fertilisers.
  - An increase in pests and diseases – necessitating the use of pesticides to remove insects and other pests.

In recent years the views of government, farmers and consumers have changed. People are far more aware of the value of the countryside, not only because it is a source of food, but also because it provides a habitat for plants and animals as well as a place to visit for relaxation and enjoyment. Schemes are in place to encourage farmers to manage their farms for biodiversity. Some land is given over to conservation and the farmers receive a grant to compensate them for reduced income. Since the Environment Act was passed in 1995 the loss of hedgerows has been reversed. Hedges are important as they provide habitats for insects and birds that live and feed on them. They also provide nesting sites for birds. Hedges act as wildlife corridors enabling birds and mammals to move from one area of woodland to another, helping to maintain the biodiversity of the woodlands.

Deforestation

Forest and woodland trees are being cut down faster than they can be replanted or regenerated naturally. Forests help to maintain a balance of carbon dioxide and oxygen in the atmosphere.

Reasons for deforestation:

- There is a world demand for timber as a building material.
- Wood is used as a fuel.
- Land is cleared for farming.
- New roads are built to provide a transport infrastructure.
- There is a demand for paper and packaging.

The consequences of deforestation are:

- Climate change. The rate at which carbon dioxide is removed from the atmosphere by the process of photosynthesis is being reduced by cutting down forests. On a global scale this is a massive reduction and contributes to global warming.

- Destruction of natural habitats, leading to a reduction in biodiversity. It is estimated that at least 50% of the Earth's species live in the tropical rain forests, even though they only occupy about 10% of the Earth's land area. If natural habitats are destroyed, this may lead to the loss of medicinal properties of some tropical plants that may become extinct before their clinical properties have been investigated.

- Soil erosion:
  - Digging and ploughing loosens the topsoil, assisting in the process of **soil erosion**.
  - The removal of vegetation affects regional climate mainly by reducing rainfall thus accelerating desertification.
  - Deforestation of the watershed causes lowland flooding.

The removal of vegetation on the higher slopes of valleys results in heavy rain sweeping exposed soil to the flood plains below. On the lower slopes, plants and leaf litter would normally act as a sponge soaking up heavy rainfall, and water would gradually be released into the soil. Instead, due to the absence of plants, only evaporation occurs. This is generally slower than transpiration in returning water vapour to the atmosphere, so soil conditions become wetter.

Key term

Soil erosion = the removal of topsoil containing valuable nutrients.

quickfire

⑧³ State three consequences of deforestation.

Grade boost

In answering a question on the effect of human influence on habitats you must give an objective and scientific answer. Too often candidates become carried away with the effects of human activity and do not provide clear and logical arguments supported by appropriate facts and examples.

quickfire

⑧⁴ How does deforestation contribute to soil erosion?

relatively heavy flow of water

relatively light flow of water

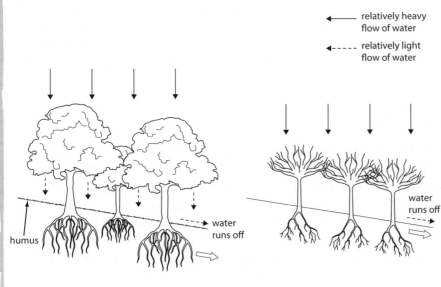

Deforestation.

Key terms

Biofuel = any kind of fuel that is biological in origin. In recent years, the term biofuel has come to mean ethanol and diesel made from crops including corn, sugarcane and rapeseed.

Coppicing = the cutting down of trees close to the ground and then left for several years to re-grow.

Long rotation time = leaving each part of the forest for many years before re-harvesting it.

Selective cutting = felling only some of the largest trees, leaving the others in place.

≫ Pointer

Woodland and forests have been used as a source of timber for thousands of years. With careful management, it is possible to make use of this resource without destroying the ecosystem.

≫ Pointer

In Europe protected areas preserve species. Efforts are also being made to conserve the dwindling areas of tropical rain forests. This involves the development of habitats which are legally safeguarded and patrolled by wardens. This gives authorities greater powers to control developments and activities within designated areas.

quickfire

85 Name a crop used to manufacture biofuel.

Forest management

Managed forestry involves sustainable replanting and regeneration:

- In Britain the technique of **coppicing** has been used for thousands of years. This traditional woodland management system is based on the fact that most deciduous trees grow from the base when their trunks are cut down.

- Instead of removing all the trees in an area at one time, **selective cutting** can be used. This technique is valuable on steep slopes where the total removal of trees would leave the soil very vulnerable to erosion. Selective cutting also helps to maintain nutrients in the forest soil, reduces the nutrient loss, and minimises the amount of soil that is washed into nearby waterways.

- **Long rotation time** also increases sustainability.

With good forestry practice, efficiency can be increased in several ways:

- Planting trees the optimum distance apart. Planting trees too close together will result in intra-specific competition. This results in the trees growing tall and thin producing poor quality timber.

- Controlling pests and diseases. If trees grow well, this results in a high quality harvest of timber. This means that fewer trees need to be felled. Best use is made of the land, reducing the total area of land required.

- Cutting timber in such a way that a similar number of trees are removed year after year for long periods of time, the forest ecosystem can be maintained. This means that the habitats are left intact and species are able to live in the forest even though timber is being extracted.

- Preservation of native woodlands. At present woodland covers 10% of the UK but of this area only 1% consists of natural or native woodland. It is essential that these native woodlands are preserved in order to maintain and enhance biodiversity. There is a need to plant more native species to provide a wide range of habitats for the great variety of species that live there.

Biofuels

Biofuels exist in a variety of forms including wood, wood chippings and straw; biogas (methane) from animals' excrement; ethanol, diesel or other liquid fuels made from processing plant material or waste oil.

- Ethanol for fuel is made through fermentation, the same process which produces it in wine and beer. Biodiesel is an oil substitute manufactured from oil seed rape. Biogas, mainly methane, is used on a small scale to power generators. Bio-ethanol, an alcohol, is usually mixed with petrol, while biodiesel is either used on its own or in a mixture.

- In theory, biofuels appear to be climate-friendly in that they reduce greenhouse gas emissions compared to conventional transport fuels. Burning the fuels releases carbon dioxide; but growing the plants absorbs a comparable amount of the gas from the atmosphere. However, energy is used in farming and processing the crops, and this can make biofuels as polluting as petroleum-based fuels, depending on what is grown and how it is treated.

- Brazil leads the world in production and use, making about 16 billion litres per year of ethanol from its sugarcane industry; 60% of new cars can run on a fuel mix which includes 85% ethanol.

- From the environmental point of the view, the big issue is biodiversity. With much of the Western world's farmland already consisting of fields of monocultured crops, the fear is that a major adoption of biofuels will reduce habitat for animals and wild plants still further.

- Asian countries may be tempted to replace rainforest with more palm oil plantations. If increased proportions of food crops such as corn or soy are used for fuel, this may push prices up, affecting food supplies for less prosperous populations.

- The mixed picture regarding the climate benefit of biofuels leads some observers to say that the priority should be reducing energy use; they claim that initiatives on biofuels detract attention from this and are more of a financial help to politically important farming lobbies than a serious attempt to cut greenhouse gas emissions.

- There are also technical problems. Although engines can generally cope with the new fuels, current technologies limit production, because only certain parts of specific plants can be used. The tough cellulose in the plant cell walls has to be pre-treated before it can be fermented. It is hoped that the so-called second-generation of biofuels will process the cellulose found in many plants. This should lead to far more efficient production using a much greater range of plants and plant waste.

Overfishing

There has been a dramatic increase in the intensity and efficiency of commercial fishing methods resulting in **overfishing** in many areas of the world.

Commercial fishing

Some fish, called pelagic fish, live in the upper parts of the water and are caught by **drift netting**. Once caught in the net the fish cannot escape unless they are small enough to fit through the net's mesh.

Fish that live deeper in the water, the mid and bottom-feeders, are caught by **trawling**. The size of the holes in the net is again very important and it is vital for the conservation of fish stocks that nets with a very small mesh are banned as they catch young fish before they have become sufficiently mature to reproduce.

Overfishing can seriously affect not only the fish stocks but also the livelihoods of the fishermen. A delicate balance needs to be struck between catching large numbers of fish so as to make a commercial living and ensuring that there are enough fish left alive to be able to replenish stocks for future years.

Key terms

Overfishing = the rate at which fish are harvested exceeds the rate at which they reproduce.

Drift netting = suspending a net from floats stretched between two boats so that fish swim into it.

Trawling = dragging a large net through the water, catching whatever happens to be in the way.

quickfire

86 Which country is the world leader in the use of biofuels?

 Grade boost

Deforestation and biofuels are linked topics in that areas have been cleared in order to produce large fields of monocultured crops.

quickfire

87 What is the main technical problem associated with the production of biofuels?

Key term

Eutrophication = the artificial enrichment of aquatic habitats by excess nutrients, often caused by run-off of fertilisers, resulting in a reduction in the oxygen level of the water. (For more detail see page 120.)

≫ *Pointer*

The European Commission has successfully banned the fishing of particular species, enabling the breeding stocks to recover. Legislation limiting the size of fishing fleets, restricting the numbers of days spent at sea, and controlling the mesh size of nets has been less successful as they are difficult to enforce.

quickfire

⑧⑧ State two measures that can be enforced to reduce overfishing.

≫ *Pointer*

In the UK trout and salmon are the fish most commonly farmed.

quickfire

⑧⑨ Name two substances added to fish stocks that can cause potential problems to the environment.

Effects of overfishing on other wildlife:

The overfishing of a particular species has 'knock-on' effects along the food chain. For example, as herring is eaten by cod, if herring are overfished, the cod population suffers as well. In the Antarctic, fishing for krill is threatening to disrupt the delicate balance of nature in these waters. Krill are small shrimps and are a very important trophic level in the food chain. They are the main source of food for the great whales, and also supplement the diets of seals, penguins, squid and fish. Krill occur in huge swarms many miles across. Since the 1980s six countries, including Japan and Russia, have been harvesting krill. The natural balance in the Antarctic has already been upset by the overexploitation of whales; the heavy fishing of krill will undoubtedly have a serious effect on the whale population.

Measures to reduce overfishing:

- Imposing quotas on catches based on scientific estimates of the size of the fish stocks.
- Restricting the net mesh size. Correct mesh size should be used in all nets to ensure that fish of the correct age are caught and to prevent as much as possible 'accidental' catches of other fish. Larger mesh nets allow juvenile fish to escape and so survive to reproduce.
- International agreements limiting catches.
- Enforcing closed seasons for fishing.
- Enforcing exclusion zones.

Fish farming

Fish can be bred and grown to maturity in ponds, lakes and managed enclosures in estuaries, where predation is reduced and food supplies are maintained. For plankton-feeders the growth of phytoplankton can be aided by the addition of artificial fertilisers to the water. Fish grow rapidly when they are reared in the warm waters discharged from factories.

- Fish farming, however, is the cause of many problems. Farmed salmon are often kept very densely stocked. In this state the fish can more easily become diseased and these diseases can spread to wild fish. Huge amounts of antibiotics are required to keep the fish moderately healthy. The pesticides used to control fish parasites are also known to harm marine invertebrates. There is also the likelihood that the delicate balance of the waterways may be upset. For example, **eutrophication** can result when fish excreta, waste food and fertiliser are carried in the water to the wider community around the rearing pens.
- When fish escape, the farmed fish interbreed with wild fish and potentially weaken wild stocks. There is also the problem of pollution in the water and seabed around fish farms. Farmed salmon, which are carnivorous, eat three times their body weight in fish feed, which is made from other fish. This is not the best use of resources from an environmental point of view. Another problem with all salmon (wild or farmed) is that they can contain high levels of dioxins and polychlorinated biphenyls (PCBs).

Effect of human activities on the carbon cycle

There has been a rise in carbon dioxide in the atmosphere, particularly over the last 50 years. There are two main reasons for the increase:

1. The burning of fossil fuels. This accounts for about 70% of the increase in CO_2, most (76%) coming from industrialised countries.

2. Deforestation – accounts for about 30% of the increased CO_2 levels, as about half the world's forests have been removed over the last 30 years. Forests help to maintain the balance of carbon dioxide and oxygen in the atmosphere. This is important because carbon dioxide is a '**greenhouse gas**'. It absorbs radiation from the Earth and if it accumulates, it leads to '**global warming**'.

- Greenhouse gases form a layer in the atmosphere acting like glass in a greenhouse. These gases allow high-energy solar radiation to pass through to the Earth's surface. Much of this energy is 'bounced back' towards space as heat but some of the energy is absorbed and trapped by the gases. The greenhouse effect is a natural process without which the average temperature on Earth would be too low to sustain life. In recent years the situation has become much worse due to the increase in industrialisation in countries such as China, and the increase in global transport.

- Global warming may lead to changes in rainfall patterns, a rise in sea level, and a wide range of impacts on plants, wildlife, and humans. When scientists talk about the issue of climate change, their concern is about global warming caused by human activities.

- Possible consequence of global warming may be:
  - Some melting of polar icecaps resulting in flooding in coastal areas.
  - Increased frequency of droughts, hurricanes and cyclones, and also forest fires.
  - In tropical areas of the world, decreased availability of water might lead to the formation of deserts.
  - Increased crop yields, but insect pest populations might also increase.

- Climate change will have serious effects on world food production with massive reductions in the grain crops of North America and Central Asia. This would have serious economic and political consequences.

- Genetic engineering research is ongoing to develop drought-resistant crops. A gene that controls water efficiency in plants has been identified but it will take many years of research to develop the idea further.

Key terms

Global warming = refers to an average increase in the Earth's temperature, which in turn causes changes in climate.

Greenhouse gas = gases such as methane, CFCs and carbon dioxide, which cause more heat energy to be trapped in the atmosphere, thus raising the temperature at the Earth's surface.

>> *Pointer*
Link the effect of human activities with previous study of the carbon cycle in BY4 page 33.

>> *Pointer*
It is suggested that if concentrations of greenhouse gases rise at current rates, possible temperature increases during the next 50 years could be in the range 1.5 – 5.5°C.

(90) State two reasons for the increase in carbon dioxide in the atmosphere.

>> *Pointer*
The increase in greenhouse gases is thought to be the cause of global warming.

Key term

Algal bloom = water becomes densely populated with species of algae as their growth is enhanced by abundant nutrients.

>> *Pointer*

The indiscriminate use of nitrogen-containing fertilisers may pollute water supplies and pose a threat to humans.

Grade boost

Revisit the nitrogen cycle on page 33 of BY4.

>> *Pointer*

Digging drainage ditches has a detrimental effect on habitats.

91 State what farmers must do to comply with regulations to reduce levels of nitrate in waterways.

Effect of using nitrogen-containing fertilisers

In developed countries agriculture has become more intensive, providing high yields of crops from relatively small areas of land. However, this increase in food production has had a deleterious effect on the environment. The increased use of nitrate-containing fertilisers has had some harmful effects on both aquatic and terrestrial ecosystems.

- Problems caused by excess nitrate in soils. On agricultural land the increased use of fertiliser has reduced species diversity on grassland. Fertilisers increase the growth of grasses and plants such as nettles which shade out smaller plants.

- Problems caused by nitrates leaching into rivers. The leaching of nitrates and phosphates from the surrounding land is a slow, natural process during which the concentration of salts builds up in bodies of water. In lakes and rivers the salts normally accumulate until equilibrium is reached, where they are exactly counterbalanced by the rate at which they are removed. However, sewage and fertilisers are an additional source of these salts and their leaching from the land into the water may result in eutrophication of lakes and rivers.

- Nitrate is highly soluble and is readily leached from soil and washed into rivers from surrounding land. The first effect may be an **algal bloom**. At this stage the water may become green, and light is unable to penetrate to any depth. The plants in the deeper regions of the lake are unable to photosynthesise and therefore die. There is a general decrease in animal species diversity as they rely on the plants for food and shelter. The short-lived algae soon die and are decomposed by saprobiontic bacteria which use a lot of oxygen, creating a biochemical oxygen demand (BOD). The water in all but the very upper layers becomes deoxygenated, so that fish and other oxygen-requiring species die. In the final stages of the process of eutrophication anaerobic bacteria in the water may reduce nitrate to nitrite (both nitrate and nitrite are toxic compounds). In view of their toxicity, the EU has set a limit of 11.3 parts per million (ppm) total nitrogen in drinking water. This figure has been exceeded in parts of the UK.

- Where the problem of high nitrate levels in waterways is particularly serious, farmers must comply with strict legislation to reduce the quantity of nitrate they release into the environment. They must:
  - Restrict the amount of fertiliser applied to the soil.
  - Only apply fertiliser at a time when the crops are actively growing.
  - Leave a strip at least 10 metres wide next to watercourses.
  - Dig drainage ditches.

Summary: Environment, Genetics and Evolution

The genetic code and cell function

- DNA is able to make copies of itself by semi-conservative replication.
- DNA acts as a template to produce mRNA, which carries the coded information from DNA in the nucleus to the ribosomes where proteins are synthesised.
- During meiosis there are two divisions, and exchange of chromosome material results in variation as a result of random segregation and crossing over.
- Meiosis results in the formation of haploid gametes – each being genetically different.

Inheritance

- A monohybrid cross is the study of the inheritance of one gene; a dihybrid cross involves the inheritance of two separate genes.
- During meiosis only one of a pair of alleles enters a gamete.
- In dihybrid inheritance either of a pair of alleles may combine randomly with either of another pair.
- Co-dominance is where the heterozygote individual has a phenotype intermediate between the two homozygous parents.
- Genes present on the same chromosome are said to be linked and are inherited together.
- Genes carried on the same sex chromosome are said to be sex linked.

Variation and evolution

- Variation is the result of both genetic change and environmental factors.
- A mutation is an unpredictable change in the genetic material of an organism.
- A gene mutation results from a change in the base sequence of DNA.
- A chromosome mutation results from a change in the chromosome structure or change in the number of whole sets of chromosomes or individual chromosomes.
- The theory of natural selection proposes that those organisms that are best adapted for survival reproduce to pass on their genes for beneficial characteristics to the next generation.
- A population of organisms reproducing sexually contains a large amount of genetic variation called the gene pool.
- The separation of two populations as a result of isolation may result in the formation of a new species.
- There are two main forms of isolation mechanisms: geographical and reproductive.

Sexual reproduction

- During sexual reproduction haploid gametes fuse to produce a diploid zygote.
- In the human, testes produce spermatozoa and the ovaries produce ova.
- Spermatogenesis is the production of sperm and oogenesis is the production of the secondary oocyte.
- Following the release of sperm into the female tract, fertilisation occurs only after the process of capacitation.
- In flowering plants, there are two main methods of pollination: insects and wind.
- Cross-pollination results in far greater genetic variation in a population than self-pollination.
- Double fertilisation is unique to flowering plants.
- The resulting seed is enclosed within an ovary and contains the zygote, which develops into the embryo plant together with the food store, the endosperm.

Applications of reproduction and genetics

- Cloning can be used to produce large numbers of genetically identical organisms in a fairly short period of time.
- Micropropagation provides a rapid method of obtaining large numbers of genetically identical plants.
- Artificial clones can be formed in animals by separating embryos at an early stage.
- The technique of growing cells in a laboratory is called tissue culture.
- Central to tissue engineering is the use of stem cells.
- Therapeutic stem cell cloning has enormous medical potential. Stem cell research raises ethical issues.
- The Human Genome Project has determined the order of bases in the Human Genome together with their identification, sequencing and mapping.
- Genetic engineering involves the extraction of a gene or genes from one organism and their transfer into a host organism.
- Recombinant DNA technology involves the introduction of DNA from various organisms into bacterial cells which will then produce a desired product.
- A transgenic or genetically modified organism has its genotype altered producing a new strain of organism. This has tremendous potential in agriculture and health.
- The aim of gene therapy is to treat a genetic disease by replacing defective genes in the patient's body with replicated non-defective genes.
- The polymerase chain reaction can produce large quantities of identical DNA from a small sample.
- A person's DNA profile or 'genetic fingerprint' is unique and can be used to provide forensic evidence and also determine parents in paternity cases.

Energy and ecosystems

- An ecosystem is a natural unit of living components in a given area as well as the non-living factors with which they interact.
- The study of the flow of energy through the ecosystem is known as ecological energetics.
- The overall efficiency of energy conversion in photosynthesis is low.
- Energy passing from one trophic level to the next results in energy lost due to respiration and excretion.
- Energy pyramids are an accurate method of representing feeding relationships.
- Succession is the change in the structure and species composition of a community over time.

Effects of human activities

- Human activity has a great influence on the environment.
- There is an increased tendency for organisms to become resistant to pesticides as a result of overuse.
- Artificial selection is the process of cross breeding plants and animals with useful characteristics.
- Human activity is the main cause of species extinction.
- The conservation of species ensures the preservation of existing gene pools.
- Conflicts exist between farming and conservation.
- Deforestation means the loss of important habitats, soil erosion and a change in the balance of atmospheric gases such as carbon dioxide.
- Increasing levels of carbon dioxide are the cause of the greenhouse effect and possibly global warming.
- Fertilisers contribute to water pollution, resulting in eutrophication.
- A dramatic increase in the intensity and efficiency of commercial fishing methods has resulted in overfishing in many areas of the world.
- The use of biofuels is theoretically a method of reducing greenhouse gas emissions but their adoption may result in a reduction in habitats for animals and plants.

Exam Practice and Technique

Exam practice and skills

How exam questions are set

WJEC A2 Biology aims to encourage students to:

- develop their interest and enthusiasm for the subject, including developing an interest in further study and careers in the subject
- appreciate how society makes decisions about scientific issues and how the sciences contribute to the success of the economy and society
- develop and demonstrate a deeper appreciation of the skills, knowledge and understanding of How Science Works
- develop essential knowledge and understanding of different areas of the subject and how they relate to each other.

Examination questions are written to reflect the assessment objectives as laid out in the specification. Candidates must meet the following assessment objectives in the context of the content detailed in the specification.

Assessment objective AO1: Knowledge and understanding of science and How Science Works

Candidates should be able to:

- recognise, recall and show understanding of scientific knowledge
- select, organise and communicate relevant information in a variety of forms.

38% of the questions set on the exam paper are recall of knowledge.

Assessment objective AO2: Application of knowledge and understanding of science and How Science Works

Candidates should be able to:

- analyse and evaluate scientific knowledge and processes
- apply scientific knowledge and processes to unfamiliar situations including those relating to issues
- assess the validity, reliability and credibility of scientific information.

56% of the questions set on the exam paper include application of knowledge.

Assessment objective AO3: How Science Works

Candidates should be able to:

- demonstrate and describe ethical, safe and skilful practical techniques and processes, selecting appropriate qualitative and quantitative methods
- make, record and communicate reliable and valid observations and measurements with appropriate precision and accuracy
- analyse, interpret, explain and evaluate the methodology, results and impact of their own and others' experimental and investigative activities in a variety of ways.

6% of the questions set on the exam paper include How Science Works.

BY4 and BY5: Written paper (1 hour 45 minutes)

The following is an approximate guide to the structure of the examination papers, BY4 and BY5:

Type of question	Marks per question	Number of questions per paper BY4	Number of questions per paper BY5
Short structured	2–5	2–4	2–4
Longer structured	7–15	2–5	2–5
Essay (1 out of 2)	10–12	1	1
Total marks		80	80

Examination questions are written by the Principal examiner well in advance of the examination. A committee of experienced examiners discuss the quality of every question as well as the suitability of the wording.

The following is advice given in the specification:

The questions are worded very carefully so that they are clear, concise and unambiguous. Despite this, candidates tend to penalise themselves unnecessarily when they misread questions, either because they read them too quickly or too superficially. It is essential that candidates appreciate the precise meaning of each word in the question if they are to be successful in producing concise, relevant and unambiguous responses. The mark value at the end of each part of each question provides a useful guide as to the amount of information required in the answer.

Synoptic assessment

In Biology, synoptic assessment requires candidates to make and use connections within and between different areas of the subject by bringing together scientific knowledge and understanding to a particular situation or context.

Examination questions for BY4 and BY5 include some marks which specifically address the requirement for synoptic assessment. These are largely skill-based questions such as comprehension and data response which require the bringing together of different parts of the course. Answers including some fundamental concepts, and content from AS units may be credited in synoptic questions.

Exam tips

Read the question carefully. Examiners try to make the wording of the questions as clear as possible but in the examination situation, it is all too easy to misinterpret a question. Read every word in every sentence carefully and use a highlighter pen if it helps you to focus on key words.

Understand the information

Only a certain percentage of the questions at A2 are based on recall of knowledge. You may encounter unfamiliar material. It is important that you do not panic but think carefully and take your time and apply the principles that you have learnt to answer these types of question. You many also encounter a graph or table. Again, read the information carefully several times before you attempt the question.

Look at the mark allocation

Each question or part of a question is allocated a number of marks. You must make sure that if the question is worth three marks, then you must give three points to gain those marks.

Understand the instructions

Know the meaning of action words. Make sure that you are familiar with the terms below and that you understand what the examiner expects you to do.

Describe

This term may be used in a variety of questions where you need to give a step-by-step account of what is taking place. In a graph question, for example, you may be required to recognise a simple trend or pattern, then you should also use the data supplied to support your answer. At this level it is insufficient to state that the graph goes up and then flattens. You are expected to describe what goes up and by how much.

Explain

A question may ask you to describe and also explain. You will not be given a mark for merely describing what happens – a biological explanation is also needed.

Suggest

This action word often occurs at the end of a question when you are expected to put forward a sensible idea based on your biological knowledge. There may not be a definite answer to this question.

Name

This means that you must give no more than a one-word answer. You do not have to repeat the question or put your answer into a sentence. This is wasting time.

State

A brief, concise answer with no explanation.

Compare

If you are asked to make a comparison, do so. For example, if you are asked to compare an insect and a wind-pollinated flower, don't simply provide two separate descriptions. What is required is a comparative statement.

Tips about structured questions

Structured questions can be short, requiring a one-word response, or can include the opportunity for extended writing. The number of lined spaces on the exam question paper together with a mark allocation are indications of the length of answer expected and the number of points to be made. Structured questions are in several parts, usually about a common content. There is an increase in the degree of difficulty as you work your way through the question. The first part may be simple recall, perhaps defining a term, the most difficult part coming at the end of the question.

Tips about essays and diagrams

All too often candidates rush into essay questions, often writing everything they know about the topic without specifically answering the question. You should take your time, reading the question carefully to discover exactly what the examiner requires in the answer. Highlight the key words then write down a plan. This will not only help you to organise your thoughts but also give you a checklist to which you can refer back while writing your answer. In this way you will be less likely to repeat yourself, wander off the subject or miss out important points.

Consider this sample question:

'Describe the main consequences of deforestation. Discuss methods which can be used to reduce the impact.'

The words to highlight are – describe, consequences, discuss, methods, reduce.

Do not rush into the essay and start to give the reasons for deforestation. The question does not ask for this. 'Describe' asks for more than a 'list'. It would be insufficient to state, climate change, destruction of habitats, soil erosion. You must describe what these mean and their effects on the environment and biodiversity. The second part of the question requires you to 'discuss' methods of reducing deforestation. Are some methods more effective than others? What is meant by 'forestry management'? What is meant by 'sustainable replanting and regeneration'? What effect do pests and diseases have on the quality and yield of timber?

When you have a plan to follow, it is so much easier to organise your thoughts while writing your answer.

Should you include a diagram in your essay answer?

Where appropriate you should include well-drawn, annotated diagrams. Even in essay questions this is an excellent way of communicating biology. In fact the rubric in the essay section states: 'Any diagrams in your answer must be fully annotated'. This means that you are encouraged to include a diagram, but a labelled diagram is insufficient. 'Annotate' means adding a short description of the function or relevant point about the structure of the labelled part.

Questions and answers

This part of the guide looks at student answers to examination-style questions through the eyes of an examiner. There is a selection of questions on topics in the A2 specification with two sample answers, one of a high grade standard and one of a lower grade standard in each case. The examiner commentary is designed to show you how marks are gained and lost so that you understand what is required in your answers.

BY4: Metabolism, Microbiology and Homeostasis

BY5: Environment, Genetics and Evolution

Q & A 1

Give an account of anaerobic respiration in organisms.   *[10 marks]*

Mark scheme

① *Glucose is phosphorylated* ② *to form hexose phosphate* ③ *which is split into triose phosphate/glycerate phosphate* ④ *which is converted to pyruvate* ⑤ *and reduced NAD* ⑥ *This takes place in the cytoplasm/glycolysis* ⑦ *in the absence of oxygen/no oxygen to act as final electron acceptor/ETC cannot take place* ⑧ *In animals pyruvate is converted to lactic acid* ⑨ *using the reduced NAD* ⑩ *In plants/fungi decarboxylation tak②es place* ⑪ *with the production of ethanal* ⑫ *Ethanal is reduced by NADH to ethanol* ⑬ *Yield of 2 ATP from glycolysis* ⑭ *Explanation of net yield 2 input 4 output* ⑮ *Energy still tied up in lactate/ethanol.*

Jack's answer

Anaerobic respiration occurs when there is a lack of oxygen available to the organism. This means that oxygen cannot be used as the final electron acceptor, so only glycolysis can take place. ✓ ⑥ The reduced NAD and FAD cannot be re-oxidised and then recycled to pick up more hydrogen because there is no oxygen to accept the hydrogen ions at the end. Therefore the concentration of hydrogen ions builds up in the mitochondrial matrix so that there is no electrochemical gradient. So the electron transport chain cannot take place. ✓ ⑦ The stage of respiration which does occur is glycolysis. As the glucose molecule is very unreactive, it is first phosphorylated ✓ ① into hexose by phosphate✓ ② and then into two molecules of triose phosphate. ✓ ③ This requires two molecules of ATP. Each molecule of triose phosphate undergoes dehydrogenation with a loss of two hydrogen ions which are accepted by NAD forming reduced NAD. ✓ ⑤ Each triose phosphate is converted into a molecule of pyruvate✓ ④ and during this process two molecules of ATP are produced. ✓ ⑬ As there are two molecules of triose phosphate, four molecules of ATP are produced for every one glucose molecule. However, as two ATPs are used in phosphorylation the overall yield of ATP from glycolysis is two ATPs. ✓ ⑭ In addition, two molecules of reduced NAD are produced. This cannot deliver hydrogen ions to the electron transport chain due to the lack of oxygen so in animals the pyruvate itself becomes the final hydrogen acceptor. The reduced NAD is oxidised back to NAD✓ ⑨ and the pyruvate forms lactic acid. ✗ ⑧

In plants the pyruvate is first decarboxylated ✓ ⑩ into ethanal ✓ ⑪ with the production of one molecule of carbon dioxide. The ethanal is then reduced to ethanol and the reduced NAD✓ ⑫ is oxidised back to NAD. Anaerobic respiration is much less efficient than aerobic respiration as it only produces two molecules of ATP instead of the 38 molecules produced in aerobic respiration. Anaerobic respiration only has 2% efficiency.

Examiner commentary

⑧ Jack fails to mention that lactic acid is produced in animals.

Summative comment

Jack has produced an excellent, detailed answer, although he does repeat himself at times.

Jack achieves 10 out of 10 marks.

Bethan's answer

Anaerobic respiration means there is no oxygen involved and only glycolysis can take place out of all the three stages of respiration. ✓ ⑥ The electron transport chain will not take place so reduced NAD cannot produce ATP. Glycolysis occurs in the cytoplasm of a cell. Glucose is a stable molecule that needs to be changed into a more unstable molecule called hexose phosphate. ✓ ② This is carried out by adding ATP, i.e. the glucose is phosphorylated. ✓ ① The unstable 6-carbon molecule is split into two, 3-carbon molecules called triose phosphate. ✓ ③ Each triose phosphate undergoes decarboxylation and dehydrogenation ✗ ⑤ carbon dioxide and pyruvate. ✓ ④ Also, each triose phosphate gives off 2 ATP by substrate level phosphorylation. ✓ ⑬ This means that there is a total of 4 ATP gained but because 2 ATP were needed to convert glucose into hexose phosphate the net gain is 2 ATP. ✓ ⑭ The pyruvate is a 2-carbon molecule and as it cannot enter the link reaction and in animals the reduced NAD is used to convert the pyruvate to lactic acid. ✓ ⑧ In higher plants pyruvate is involved in a different mechanism whereby it undergoes dehydrogenation and decarboxylation to form ethanol. ✗✗ ⑩ ⑪ Anaerobic respiration produces only 2 ATP compared to aerobic which produces 38 ATP. Therefore anaerobic respiration is a much less efficient process.

Examiner commentary

⑤ Bethan fails to state that dehydrogenation results in the formation of reduced NAD. ⑩ ⑪ Bethan states that pyruvic acid is converted to ethanol directly rather than through the intermediate, ethanal. She does not state exactly where carbon dioxide is given off and where dehydrogenation takes place.

Summative comment

Bethan's essay contains few errors but requires extra detail in places.

Bethan achieves 8 out of 10 marks.

Q&A 2

(a) Describe the reactions that link glycolysis to the Krebs cycle. [3]

(b) Where precisely in the cell does each of the following take place? [2]
  (i) Glycolysis   (ii) Krebs cycle

acetyl (2C) CoA   CoA
oxaloacetate (4C)   citrate(6C)
P
T
intermediate (5C)
Q
intermediate (4C) (4C)
intermediate (4C)
S
intermediate (4C)   R

(c) The diagram shows an outline of the Krebs cycle
A two-carbon acetyl group enters the cycle by combining with a molecule of oxaloacetate (4C) with the formation of citrate (6C). This is then decarboxylated and dehydrogenated to regenerate the oxaloacetate.

(i) Explain the following terms: [2]
  I. decarboxylation
  II dehydrogenation

(ii) State the letters of the individual steps in the cycle where decarboxylation is taking place. [1]

(d) ATP is made directly by substrate level phosphorylation in the Krebs cycle.

(i) State the number of ATP molecules that are made directly per 'turn' of the cycle. [1]

(ii) Complete the table to show the number of ATP molecules that are made electron transport chain per 'turn' of the cycle. [2]

	In the link reaction using NADH	In the Krebs Cycle using NADH	In the Krebs Cycle using FADH
Number of molecules of ATP formed			

(iii) Explain why the two hydrogen acceptors NAD and FAD lead to the production of different numbers of ATP molecules. [1]

[total = 12 marks]

Jack's answer

(a) Pyruvate loses a molecule of carbon dioxide ✓ and is converted to acetate ✓ with the formation of reduced NAD. ✓ The acetate group combines with CoA to produce acetyl CoA.

(b) (i) Cytoplasm ✓
  (ii) Matrix of mitochondrion ✓

(c) (i) I The removal of carbon dioxide ✓
    II The removal of hydrogen ✓
  (ii) P and Q ✓

(d) (i) One ✓
  (ii) 3 9 2 ✓✓
  (iii) Because NAD has more pumps than FAD. ✗ ①

Examiner commentary

① It is insufficient to state that one carrier system has more pumps than another. The carrier system involving NAD has three pumps whereas that involving FAD has two pumps. Where FAD is the first carrier it is not associated with a pump.

Jack achieves 11 out of 12 marks.

Bethan's answer

(a) Pyruvate is converted to acetate. ✓ The acetate group combines with CoA to produce acetyl CoA. ✓ ①

(b) (i) Cytoplasm ✓
  (ii) Mitochondrion ✗ ②

(c) (i) I The removal of carbon ✗ ③
    II The removal of hydrogen ✓
  (ii) P and Q ✓

(d) (i) Six ✗ ④
  (ii) 6 18 4 ✗✗ ⑤
  (ii) FAD and NAD are two different chemicals so they produce different numbers of ATP molecules. ✗ ⑥

Examiner commentary

① Bethan has omitted the loss of carbon dioxide and the formation of reduced NAD and achieves 2 out of the 3 marks available. ② She has not been precise in her answer and has not referred to the matrix of the mitochondrion. ③ Decarboxylation is the removal of carbon dioxide. ④ Bethan has guessed the answer as she does not understand the term 'substrate level phosphorylation'. ⑤ One molecule of glucose is broken down to two molecules of pyruvate which is converted to acetate which enters the cycle as acetyl CoA. 'Per turn of the cycle' refers to one molecule entering the cycle. Bethan has not understood this and has given double the number of molecules of ATP required. ⑥ Bethan does not know that NAD carrier system has three pumps, one more than the FAD carrier system.

Bethan achieves 5 out of 12 marks.

Q&A 3

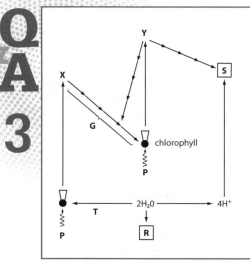

The diagram represents the light stage of photosynthesis.

(a) What is represented by the arrows labelled P? [1]
(b) What is the general name given to structures X and Y? [1]
(c) Briefly explain what is happening in the process labelled G. [1]
(d) What is represented by R? [1]
(e) What is represented by S? [1]
(f) What process is represented by the arrow labelled T? [1]
(g) Atrazine is a weed killer which prevents non-cyclic photophosphorylation from taking place. Using your knowledge of the light-independent stage of photosynthesis, explain why the use of the chemical leads to the death of a plant. [5]

[total = 11 marks]

Jack's answer

(a) P = light energy. ✓
(b) Electron acceptors. ✓
(c) Electrons flow down an electron transport chain generating ATP by non-cyclic photophosphorylation. ✓
(d) Oxygen. ✓
(e) Reduced NADP. ✓
(f) Electrons go to the photosystem. ✗ ①
(g) If non-cyclic photophosphorylation does not take place then ATP✓ and reduced NADP✓ are not produced. Then the Calvin cycle cannot take place. ✓✗✗ ②

Examiner commentary

① Jack has not stated that the electrons (from photolysis) replace those lost from photosystem II.
② Jack has made a good start but has not made five points to gain full marks. He has failed to state that as the Calvin cycle stops, glycerate phosphate cannot be converted to triose phosphate and no hexose sugar can be formed. Therefore there is no respiratory substrate available for the plant to respire.

Jack achieves 8 out of 11 marks.

Bethan's answer

(a) P = light ✗ ①
(b) Electron acceptors ✓
(c) Electrons flow along an electron transport chain ✓
(d) Oxygen ✓
(e) Reduced NAD ✗ ②
(f) Electrons go to the photosystem to replace those that go up to the electron acceptor. ✓
(g) Weed killers kill the plant by making it grow to fast so that it runs out of glucose. ✗✗✗✗✗ ③

Examiner commentary

① Bethan has not stated light 'energy'. ② She has confused NAD used in respiration with NADP. ③ Despite having been given some guidance in the question she has made no reference to the production of ATP and reduced NADP and their role in the Calvin cycle.

Bethan achieves 4 out of 11 marks.

Q&A 4

Describe how the principles of batch culture fermentation are applied in the industrial production of penicillin.

[10 marks]

Mark scheme

① All materials are present at start/not added during the process ② Sterile apparatus ③ Pure culture of Penicillium (notatum) ④ Sterile nutrient medium ⑤ Aeration method/oxygen for respiration ⑥ pH adjustment/buffer ⑦ Filters for introducing sterile air ⑧ Method of mixing to reduce sedimentation ⑨ Water jacket to control temperature and reference to enzyme denaturation/heat energy production by metabolism ⑩ Penicillin is a secondary metabolite ⑪ produced when glucose is depleted/at end of growth phase ⑫ Penicillin harvested after nutrient depletion ⑬ Filter culture fluid ⑭ Extract penicillin ⑮ Reference to penicillin production by free living fungus to reduce competition.

Jack's answer

Several requirements are necessary in batch culture fermentation. It is important that the equipment is sterile. ✓ ② All materials must be added at the start and the reaction must be left. ✓ ① A pure culture of Penicillium is used together with a sterile nutrient medium. ✓ ✓ ③ ④ The oxygen is pumped in via a sterile air filter to ensure that there is no contamination to prevent the bacteria from growing. The oxygen is required for respiration. ✓ ⑤ The fermenter also contains two probes, one for pH and one for temperature. The pH probe detects if the medium has become too acidic and if it has alkali will be added to get the pH back to its optimum. ✓ ⑥ The probe for detecting the temperature is attached to a cooling jacket. As respiration of the fungus takes place it gives off heat and the cooling jacket brings the temperature back down to the optimum for growth. ✓ ⑨ Within the fermenter is a sparger, which acts as a large stirrer continually mixing the culture and medium to ensure they are evenly distributed. ✓ ⑧ At the end of the process the penicillin is filtered out as a precipitate and then purified for use. Penicillin is a secondary metabolite ✓ ⑩ that starts to be produced after approximately 30 hours and during the stationary phase of growth when glucose becomes depleted. ✓ ⑪

Bethan's answer

Firstly, the fermenter must be washed to avoid contamination. ✗ ② The organism Penicillium produces penicillin at the end of the growth phase. ✓ ⑪ Penicillium is an obligate aerobe so requires oxygen from a sterile air inlet. ✓ ⑤ Spargers are used to further distribute oxygen. A water jacket is used to keep the temperature constant. ✗ ⑨ Probes are used to measure temperature and pH. ✗ ⑥ A filtered outlet for waste gases prevents contamination to the environment whereas sterile air prevents contamination to the Penicillium. ✓ ⑦ It takes about three days for Penicillium to reach its optimum production of penicillin at 21°C.

Examiner commentary

⑨ Jack could have stated that heat production during respiration would denature the enzymes of the fungus. ⑮ The free-living fungus produces penicillin to reduce competition when food resources are becoming scarce.

Summative comment

Jack has an excellent understanding of the process and has described clearly the functions for the various components of the fermenter.

Jack achieves 10 out of 10 marks.

Examiner commentary

② The equipment must be sterilised at the start, washing is insufficient. ⑨ Bethan has not discussed the production of heat by respiration and its consequences. ⑥ She refers to probes to monitor pH but does not state how the pH may be adjusted.

Summative comment

Bethan has made a few valid points but has produced a very superficial account.

Bethan achieves 3 out of 10 marks.

Q&A 5

A microbiologist wanted to estimate the number of bacteria present in 1cm³ of fresh milk.

A 1.0 cm³ sample of fresh milk was serially diluted to produce a range of dilutions.

A sterile pipette was used to transfer 0.5 cm³ of the 10^{-2} dilution to a sterile Petri dish containing nutrient agar.

The lid was immediately replaced, fastened down with adhesive tape, and the dish was gently rotated several times.

The same procedure was repeated with four other samples of the same dilution.

The dishes were placed in an incubator at 25°C for a period of 48 hours.

The diagram shows the appearance of the plates at the end of this time.

plate 1 plate 2
plate 3
small discrete colonies of bacteria
merging of bacterial colonies
plate 4 plate 5

(a) (i) Explain how a colony develops. [1]

(ii) Estimate the mean number of bacteria per cm³ of fresh milk.

I. Indicate which plates should be used and give a reason for your choice. [1]

II. Calculate your answer, showing your working. [3]

(b) (i) Explain why sterile equipment is used. [1]

(ii) Explain why the dishes were incubated at 25°C. [1]

(c) The bacteria normally found in milk are harmless to humans.

(i) Suggest why the lids of the dishes were fastened down following the addition of the diluted milk. [1]

(ii) Explain why, at the end of the investigation, the dishes should be autoclaved at 121°C for 15 minutes. [1]

[total = 9 marks]

Jack's answer

(a) (i) One bacterium has reproduced asexually to form a clone. ✓

(ii) I Plates 1, 2 and 4, as clumping has taken place in plates 3 and 5. ✓

II The average of the three plates is

28 + 30 + 26 = 84 ÷ 3 = 28 ✓

Dilution factor is 100 x 2 = 200✓

Answer = 28 x 200 = 5,600 per cm³. ✓

(b) (i) Other micro-organisms would contaminate the sample. ✓

(ii) This is the best temperature for the bacteria to multiply. ✗ ①

(c) (i) Bacteria from the air could get into the petri dish. ✓

(ii) Bacterial spores are resistant to boiling and need to be sterilised under pressure. ✓

Examiner commentary

① The optimum temperature for bacteria to multiply is higher than 25°C but at this higher temperature harmful bacteria (pathogens) are more likely to reproduce.

Jack achieves 8 out of 9 marks.

Bethan's answer

(a)(i) Many bacteria form a round colony. ✗ ①

(ii) I plates I, 2 and 4 ✗ ②

II 2,800 per cm³. ✗✗✗ ③

(b) (i) So that there are no microbes there at the start. ✓

(ii) So that the bacteria multiply more slowly. ✗ ④

(c) (i) To stop contamination from the environment. ✓

(ii) To make sure the bacteria are all killed. ✗ ⑤

Examiner commentary

① Bethan should state that the colony has reproduced asexually from one bacterium. ② Although she has chosen the correct dishes she has failed to give a reason for her choice. ③ She has not shown her working and so has lost the first two marks and in so doing has not taken the dilution factor into account. ④ Bethan does not know experiments with bacteria should be carried out at low temperature to prevent the growth of pathogens. ⑤ She does not know that resistant spores are not destroyed at 100°C.

Bethan achieves 2 out of 9 marks.

Q & A 6

Describe the nitrogen cycle; include the form that nitrogen takes in each part and the roles of bacteria (giving names where possible). *[10 marks]*

Mark scheme

① *Nitrogen gas in the atmosphere* ② *Amino acids/protein in plants/animals* ③ *Urea in urine/ammonia/nitrite/nitrate in soil* ④ *decomposition/putrefaction qualified* ⑤ *Nitrifying bacteria/nitrification/qualified* ⑥ *Nitrobacter and Nitrosomonas correctly linked to process* ⑦ *Ammonium compounds to nitrites* ⑧ *Nitrites to nitrates* ⑨ *Denitrifying by Pseudomonas* ⑩ *Anaerobic conditions* ⑪ *Nitrogen fixation/nitrogen fixing bacteria* ⑫ *Convert nitrogen into nitrogen-containing compounds* ⑬ *Azotobacter are free living* ⑭ *Rhizobium in root nodules/symbiotic* ⑮ *Decay bacteria release nitrogen compounds/ammonia from dead bodies, faeces and urine.*

Jack's answer

The nitrogen cycle is the flow of organic and inorganic nitrogen within an ecosystem where there is an interchange between atmospheric nitrogen and nitrogenous compounds. ✓ ① Plants and animals need nitrogen to synthesise amino acids, proteins and nucleic acids. ✓ ② Plants cannot take in atmospheric nitrogen; they can only take in nitrogen in the form of nitrates. When animals consume plants the nitrogenous compounds are passed along the food chain.

Bacteria are the key organisms involved in the nitrogen cycle. Bacteria and fungi decompose dead plants and animals, faeces and urine into ammonium ions by a process called putrefaction. ✓ ④ The ammonium ions are first converted to nitrites and then nitrates by a process called nitrification. ⑤ Nitrifying bacteria called Nitrosomonas converts ammonium ions to nitrites and different nitrifying bacteria called Nitrobacter ✓ ⑥ convert nitrites to nitrates. ✓ ⑧ These nitrates are then available in the soil for plants to use. Within the soil there are free living nitrogen fixing bacteria ✓ ⑬ called Azotobacter which can fix atmospheric nitrogen into nitrogenous compounds directly. ✓ ⑫ Another type of nitrogen fixing bacteria are called Rhizobium and these are symbiotic bacteria found in the root nodules of leguminous plants. ✓ ⑭ Denitrification is the loss of nitrogen caused by denitrifying bacteria called Pseudomonas ✓ ⑨ which can reduce nitrates back to ammonium ions and then atmospheric nitrogen. Pseudomonas, unlike nitrifying bacteria, require anaerobic conditions. ✓ ⑩ Therefore, denitrification is a problem in waterlogged soils where there are anaerobic conditions.

Farmers can plough fields to improve aeration of the soil so that the denitrifying bacteria cannot compete with the nitrifying aerobic bacteria thus preventing denitrification.

Examiner commentary

Jack has an excellent understanding of the topic and has written clearly and in an organised way. He has also linked the correct bacteria with the processes involved.

Summative comment

Jack has achieved full marks for this essay.

Bethan's answer

Nitrogen in the atmosphere is very un-reactive. Outside living organisms only lightning has the energy to convert nitrogen and fix it into forms that living organisms use, such as nitrites and nitrates. Azotobacter is free living in soils ✓ ⑬ and can change nitrogen to nitrites and nitrates. ✓ ⑫ Rhizobium has a symbiotic relationship with leguminous plants. ✗ ⑭ The legumes benefit as they get a source of nitrates and the Rhizobium benefits with a secure home and a source of carbohydrates.

Putrefaction is the decomposition of dead organisms and waste products and the final product is ammonium. ✓ ④ Many organisms, such as bacteria and fungi, can do this conversion. Nitrification is the second step which is the conversion of ammonium into nitrites and nitrates. ✓ ⑤

Denitrification takes place in waterlogged areas where anaerobic conditions prevail. ✓ ⑪ Nitrites and nitrates are converted back to nitrogen and released into the atmosphere. Pseudomonas is the organism responsible for this. ✓ ⑨

Examiner commentary

⑭ Bethan has not explained that Rhizobium is found in root nodules of leguminous plants.

Summative comment

Bethan's answer is far too brief and disorganised. She has obviously attempted to learn the topic as she mentions the bacterial species in the correct context. Had she written a plan at the outset she could have achieved a higher mark.

Bethan achieves 6 out of 10 marks.

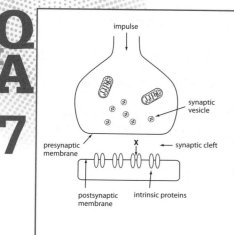

impulse

synaptic vesicle

presynaptic membrane

X

synaptic cleft

postsynaptic membrane

intrinsic proteins

Q&A 7

The diagram represents a synapse in the nervous system of a mammal.

(a) When the nerve impulse reaches a synapse, synaptic vesicles fuse with the presynaptic membrane and shed their contents into the synaptic cleft. State the **general** names given to:

(i) The contents of the synaptic vesicle. [1]

(ii) The shedding of contents into the synaptic cleft. [1]

(b) Explain fully the cause of the shedding of the vesicle contents. [2]

(c) (i) The diagram shows X passing through these channels. Name X. [1]

(ii) Give the name for this type of movement across a membrane. [2]

(iii) Explain how this movement is triggered in the membrane. [2]

(d) Explain how synaptic transmission can be disrupted using an enzyme inhibitor. [1]

(e) Caffeine, present in tea and coffee and cola drinks, increases the metabolic rate in presynaptic cells. Explain how strong coffee stimulates the nervous system. [2]

[total = 12 marks]

Jack's answer

(a) (i) Neurotransmitter. ✓

(ii) Exocytosis. ✓

(b) The presynaptic membrane is depolarised and calcium ions diffuse into the presynaptic knob from the synaptic cleft. This results in the synaptic vesicles moving down and fusing with the presynaptic membrane. ✓✓

(c) (i) Na+ ions ✓

(ii) Diffusion ✗✓ ①

(iii) There are receptors next to the intrinsic proteins. The acetylcholine fuses with these allowing the channels of the intrinsic proteins to open. ✓✓

(d) It inhibits the enzyme which breaks down acetylcholine. ✓

(e) Increases metabolism means that here is an increase in the production of ATP. ✗✓ ②

Bethan's answer

(a) (i) Acetylcholine ✗ ①

(ii) Exocytosis ✓

(b) Calcium diffuses in causing the vesicles to move down ✗✗ ②

(c) (i) Sodium ✗ ③

(ii) Active transport ✗✗ ④

(iii) The channels of the intrinsic proteins open. ✓✗ ⑤

(d) It blocks the enzyme which breaks down acetylcholine. ✓

(e) If the nervous system is stimulated there are more impulses passing along the nerves ✗✗ ⑥

Examiner commentary

① Jack has not stated that facilitated diffusion is taking place and gains only one mark. ② He does not gain the second mark here as he has not stated that as a result of more ATP synthesis more transmitter is synthesised when it is reformed from ethanoic acid and choline.

Jack achieves 10 out of 12 marks.

Examiner commentary

① Bethan has not read the question carefully. It clearly states in bold that the general and not specific name is required. ② She must use the term 'calcium ions'. She has also failed to state that the vesicles fuse with the presynaptic membrane. ③ Again she has not stated 'ions'. ④ Her answer should have been 'facilitated diffusion'. ⑤ She has not first stated that the sodium ions fuse with receptors in the membrane. ⑥ Bethan has made a guess here.

Bethan achieves 3 out of 12 marks.

Q & A 8

Part of a particular sequence of bases on a DNA molecule is as follows:
TTATCTTTCGGGATG

(a) State the sequence of nitrogenous bases on the mRNA which is obtained by using this DNA molecule as a template. [1]

(b) A sequence of nitrogenous bases on another section of mRNA is shown below;
    UACAGAGCAUCGUUA

Using the table, determine the order the amino acids would be incorporated into the polypeptide constructed from this mRNA sequence. You may assume that the sequence is read from the left-hand side. [1]

mRNA codons	Amino acid
AAG	lysine
AAU	asparagine
ACA	threonine
AGA	arginine
AUA	isoleucine
GCA	alanine
UUG	leucine
UCU	serine
UAC	tyrosine

(c) Suggest how the cell ensures that the code is read in the correct direction. [1]

(d) Proflavin is a chemical that alters the base sequence of DNA. What is the name given to such a change? [1]

(e) If proflavin caused the deletion of the first adenine in the DNA sequence which codes for the above mRNA, what consequences would this have on the subsequent translation of the sequence? [1]

[total = 5 marks]

Jack's answer

(a) AAUAGAAAGCCCUAC. ✓

(b) Tyrosine, arginine, alanine, serine, leucine. ✓

(c) This is determined by the ribosome. ✗ ①

(d) Gene mutation. ✓

(e) There would be a different sequence of amino acids as the codon would be different for the first amino acid. ✓

Examiner commentary

① There is a start codon which acts like a capital letter at the beginning of a sentence.

Jack achieves 4 out of 5 marks.

Bethan's answer

(a) AAUAGAAAGCCCUAC ✓

(b) Tyrosine, arginine, alanine, serine, leucine. ✓

(c) Because it says in the question that the sequence is read from the left hand side. ✗ ①

(d) Mutation ✗ ②

(e) The first amino acid would be different but the rest would be the same. ✗ ③

Examiner commentary

① Bethan does not know the answer! ② She has not specified the type of mutation.

③ She does not appreciate that the deletion of one base changes the order of all the other bases as the code is a triplet code.

Bethan achieves 2 out of 5 marks.

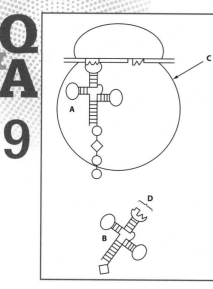

The diagram represents a stage in the synthesis of a polypeptide chain.

(a) Name:
   (i)   The organelle labelled C.   *[1]*
   (ii) The structure labelled D.   *[1]*
   (iii) The three types of RNA involved.   *[2]*
(b) The process shown arranges the correct sequence of amino acids in the peptide.
   (i)   Name the process.   *[1]*
   (ii) Explain what ensures that the correct amino acid is added. *[3]*
(c) After the stage shown, explain what happens to A and B.   *[3]*
(d) Explain why it is important that this whole process is carried out correctly.   *[1]*

[total = 12 marks]

Jack's answer

(a) (i) Ribosome ✓
   (ii) Anticodon ✓
   (iii) mRNA, tRNA ✓✗ ①
(b) (i) Translation ✓
   (ii) Each different tRNA has a specific linkage with one type of amino acid. ✓ This matches with the codon on the mRNA. ✓ The triplet of bases on both of these are complementary to each other and so they join to form a codon-anticodon complex. ✓
(c) B moves into the ribosome next to A✓ and leaves its attached amino acid. ✗✗ ②
(d) The wrong protein will be formed as the sequence of amino acids in the polypeptide will be different. ✗ ③

Examiner commentary

① Jack has named only two types of RNA, he has not named ribosomal RNA and has a mark deducted. ② He has not made three separate points required to gain three marks. B leaves the amino acid on the ribosome and this amino acid joins the chain of amino acids being formed (shown in the diagram) by means of a peptide bond. A is now free to move back into the cytoplasm and pick up another specific amino acid. B then occupies the position A was in and the ribosome moves one codon to the right. ③ Jack has failed to state that the protein formed, being a different structure, is unable to perform its intended function.

Jack achieves 8 out of 12 marks.

Bethan's answer

(a) (i) Ribosome ✓
   (ii) Anticodon ✓
   (iii) mRNA, transport RNA ✗✗ ①
(b) (i) Transcription ✗ ②
   (ii) The transport RNA carries an amino acid. and joins with the codon to form a codon-anticodon complex. ✓✗✗ ③
(c) A leaves its amino acid on the ribosome to join with the others and then goes back to pick up another amino acid. ✗✗✗ ④
(d) Because a different protein will be formed. ✗ ⑤

Examiner commentary

① Bethan has named only one type of RNA as she has named transfer RNA incorrectly. She achieves no marks. ② She has confused transcription and translation. ③ She has made only one correct statement, the formation of a complex. She has little idea of how a specific amino acid is added to tRNA (see Jack's answer). ④ She does not know the answer (see exam commentary for Jack). ⑤ She has failed to state that as the protein has a different structure it will not perform its intended function.

Bethan achieves 3 out of 12 marks.

Q&A 10

A

B

C

D

The diagrams A to D are of nuclei undergoing mitosis or meiosis.

(a) What is meant by the term 'homologous chromosomes'? [1]

(b) Which of the diagrams A–D shows cells undergoing prophase I of meiosis? [1]

(c) The diploid number of chromosomes in a mosquito is 6 (2n = 6) and in a kangaroo 12 (2n = 12). State which of the diagrams A, B, C or D represents the following: [2]

  (i) Haploid cell from a kangaroo.

  (ii) Diploid cell from a mosquito.

(d) (i) A species of ant (*Myrmecia pilosula*) has a diploid number 2. Why is it not possible to have an organism with a diploid number less than this? [1]

  (ii) In this species of ant the male is haploid. Suggest the type of cell division this organism would use to produce sperm cells. [1]

(e) The following gives the names of some stages of cell division:

Anaphase I	Metaphase II	Anaphase II	Prophase I	Telophase II	Metaphase I
M	N	P	Q	R	S

  (i) Using only the letters, give the correct sequence of the stages. [1]

  (ii) State the letter of the stage when each of the following processes occurs: [5]

    Pairing of chromosomes

    Centromeres divide

    Crossing over

    Bivalents align on equator

    Nuclear membrane reforms

[total = 12 marks]

Jack's answer

(a) A pair of identical chromosomes. ✗ ①

(b) B and D ✓

(c) Kangaroo – C. ✓
   Mosquito – A. ✓

(d) (i) Because meiosis can't take place. ✗ ②

  (ii) Mitosis. ✓

(e) (i) QSMNPR ✓

  (ii) Q P Q S R ✓✓✓✓

Examiner commentary

① Jack probably understands what 'homologous chromosomes' means but has not learnt the definition which is – 'a pair of chromosomes, one from the father and one from the mother having the same loci and therefore determining the same features'. ② He does not explain why meiosis can't take place – diploid means a pair of chromosomes which separate into haploid gametes. A single chromosome cannot divide any further.

Jack achieves 10 out of 12 marks.

Bethan's answer

(a) Chromosomes which are in pairs with one from the mother and the other from the father. ✗ ①

(b) A ✗ ②

(c) Kangaroo – C ✓
   Mosquito – A ✓

(d) (i) A diploid number of one couldn't split into two halves so meiosis won't take place. ✓

  (ii) Miosis ✓ ③

(e) (i) QMSRPN ✗ ④

  (ii) M N Q S R ✗✗✓✓✓ ⑤

Examiner commentary

① Bethan has not quite given the full definition. ② Bethan does not appreciate that during meiosis I homologous chromosomes arrange themselves in pairs. ③ She has repeated an error made in earlier questions where she is unsure of the answer and is 'hedging her bets'. ④ Bethan has not learnt the sequence and does not seem to realise that meiosis occurs in two stages, meiosis I and meiosis II. ⑤ She has given some of the correct answers. If she had reviewed her previous answer in the light of the information in this part of the question and corrected it she may have gained additional marks.

Bethan achieves 7 out of 12 marks.

Q&A 11

Describe the processes of (i) pollination and fertilisation and (ii) the development of the seed and fruit, in plants.

[10 marks]

Mark scheme

① *Pollination is the transfer of pollen from anther to stigma* ② *Two examples of pollinating mechanisms from wind, insect, self* ③ *After landing on stigma pollen grain absorbs water* ④ *Formation of pollen tube* ⑤ *Tube nucleus controls growth* ⑥ *Release of enzymes* ⑦ *Digests route through plant tissues* ⑧ *Pollen tube passes through micropyle* ⑨ *Male nucleus fuses with egg cell nucleus* ⑩ *Forms zygote which develops into embryo plant* ⑪ *Embryo plant equals plumule and radicle* ⑫ *Other male gamete fuses with both polar nucleii* ⑬ *to form triploid endosperm nucleus* ⑭ *Develops into food store* ⑮ *Fertilised ovule becomes seed and ovary becomes fruit.*

Jack's answer

Pollination is the process by which male gametes are transferred from the anther of one flower to the stigma of the same flower or another flower. ✓ ① In insect-pollinated plants the pollen sticks to the body of the insect and is transferred to the stigma of another flower when it brushes against it. In wind-pollinated plants the pollen is blown from the external anthers of a flower to the stigma of another flower. ✓ ② The pollen grain which has landed on the stigma by either method firstly takes up water ✓ ③ and then germinates to form a pollen tube. ✓ ④ In the pollen tube the tube nucleus controls the growth of the tube ✓ ⑤ and digests the plant tissues by means of an enzyme. ✓ ⑥ Following the tube nucleus are two haploid male nuclei formed from the generative nucleus. The pollen tube passes through the micropyle ✓ ⑧ into the ovary. The tube nucleus disintegrates and the two male nuclei move into the ovary, one fertilising the egg cell ✓ ⑨ and becomes the zygote, and the other fuses with both polar nuclei ✓ ⑬ to form a triploid endosperm nucleus ✓ ⑭. The zygote becomes the embryo plant ✓ ⑩ with a young shoot or plumule and young root or radicle. ✓ ⑪ The triploid nucleus develops into the food store. ✓ ⑭ The ovule becomes the seed and the ovary swells to form the fruit. ✓ ⑮

Examiner commentary

Although he gains the mark, Jack is incorrect when he states that the pollen tube and the two male nuclei pass into the ovary. The part of the ovule which contains the nuclei is in fact the embryo sac.

Summative comment

Jack has provided an almost perfect answer. His points are concise and detailed.

Jack achieves 10 out of 10 marks.

Bethan's answer

Pollination occurs when the pollen of a plant lands on the stigma of either the same flower or a different flower. ✓ ① They can undergo either self-pollination or cross-pollination. ✗ ② When the pollen grain lands on the stigma it absorbs water ✓ ③ and germinates. ✗ ④ The tube nucleus begins to grow down through the style. It releases enzymes to digest a pathway. ✓ ⑦ The pollen tube goes through the micropyle ✓ ⑧ and when the tip touches the embryo sac it causes the tip to burst releasing the male nucleus into the embryo sac where it fuses with the female egg nucleus ✓ ⑫ to form a diploid zygote. ✗ ⑩ The integuments around the ovary become the testa which is the seed shell and the ovary becomes the fruit. ✗ ⑮

Examiner commentary

② Bethan fails to give examples of pollinating mechanisms. ④ She does not mention the formation of a pollen tube. ⑩ She fails to state that the zygote develops into the embryo plant. ⑮ Although she states that the ovary becomes the fruit she makes no reference to the seed.

Summative comment

Bethan has some understanding of the processes of pollination and fertilisation but her answers lack detail. She fails to mention the other male nucleus in the pollen tube and its function if fusing with the two polar nuclei with the formation of the endosperm. Her answer also lacks detail when she refers to the embryo plant.

Bethan achieves 5 out of 10 marks.

Q & A 12

The cultivated banana is sterile and seedless. It reproduces asexually, producing shoots or suckers that develop into new plants. it is extremely difficult to develop disease-resistant varieties of this plant.

In the 1950s the main variety grown in banana plantations was Gros Michel. This variety was totally wiped out by Panama disease, caused by a soil fungus. The disease spread rapidly from one plant to another and from plantation to plantation.

Following the devastation, a variety of banana called Cavendish was found to be resistant to Panama disease and was planted and has been cultivated ever since. However, it became apparent that Cavendish was susceptible to the disease, Sigatoka, caused by another fungus. Only the use of massive amounts of fungicide spray is keeping Sigatoka under control. It seems that as soon as a new fungicide is used, the fungus develops resistance to it.

(a) State the type of cell division used in the reproduction of the banana plant. [1]

(b) Explain why Panama disease spread so quickly through the banana plantations and wiped out the Gros Michel variety in the 1950s. [3]

(c) Explain how the fungus that causes Sigatoka becomes resistant to fungicides. [5]

(d) (i) Explain why it is so difficult to develop disease-resistant varieties of banana. [2]

   (ii) Suggest a way by which disease resistance could be achieved. [1]

[total = 12 marks]

Jack's answer

(a) Mitosis. ✓

(b) Asexual reproduction is taking place and all the banana plants are genetically identical. ✓ ① All the plants have the same susceptibility to disease. ✓ The plants are planted close together so the disease spreads very easily. ✓

(c) There is variation between individuals of the fungus. ✓ There may be mutations for resistance in the population. ✓ Normally these mutations serve no purpose but if the fungicide is applied it exerts a selective pressure. ✓ Those individuals with the mutation have a selective advantage ✓ and survive. They can then pass on the mutation to the next generation when they reproduce. ✓ ②

(d) (i) Bananas are sterile and reproduce asexually. ✓ The banana plants are unable to reproduce sexually and produce gametes. ✓ ③

   (ii) Through genetic engineering by inserting a resistant gene into the plant. ✓

Examiner commentary

Jack has a good understanding of the passage and has obviously read it carefully. He has noted that the cultivated banana is sterile and reproduces asexually and this is the key to the answer. ① He could have expanded his answer and stated that the plants are clones. ② Jack has not mentioned that the mutated allele frequency would increase in the population, the more fungicide that is applied. He could also have stated that natural selection is taking place. ③ He could have mentioned that normally resistance is achieved through breeding programmes using a reservoir of alleles.

Jack achieves 12 out of 12 marks.

Bethan's answer

(a) Miosis ✗ ①

(b) The disease spreads rapidly as the fungal spores are carried in the air and bananas are grown in hot, damp places, ideal for the growth of fungi. ✗✗✗ ②

(c) Due to natural selection ✓ there is variation in the fungus. ✗ ③ Some fungi are more resistant than others and these survive to pass on their resistance ✓ to their offspring.

(d) (i) Bananas are sterile ✓ so they cannot be crossed with another banana plant. ✗ ④

   (ii) By applying more fungicide. ✗ ⑤

Examiner commentary

① Bethan has misspelt the term and cannot be awarded a mark as it could be read as meiosis. ② Bethan has not read the passage thoroughly and has completely missed the point of the question. ③ Bethan has the idea of natural selection but fails to develop the concept and does not make it clear that the variation is between individuals in the population. She fails to use terms such as 'selection pressure' and 'selective advantage' expected at this level. ④ Again, Bethan fails to develop the implication of sterility and does not use terms such as 'gene' or 'allele'. ⑤ Bethan shows her lack of understanding of the problem.

Bethan achieves 3 out of 12 marks.

Thousands of years ago a lake in Africa was separated from the main lake, Lake Victoria. A number of different species of fish have descended from a different species in the main lake.

(a) Explain why the fish from each lake can be described as different species. *[2]*

(b) Explain how the splitting of the fish population into the two lake populations has led to the formation of the separate species. *[4]*

[total = 6 marks]

Jack's answer

(a) They are unable to interbreed with each other to produce fertile offspring. ✓✓

(b) The populations have been physically separated from each other. ✓ This type of isolation is called geographical isolation. This means that the fish cannot interbreed. ✓ In the two lakes environmental conditions might be different and there will be different selection pressures exerted. ✓ By chance different random mutations may arise leading to differences in the two gene pools. ✓ Over a long period of time the physical appearance of the fish may alter or their behaviour may change.

Examiner commentary

Jack has an excellent understanding of isolation and speciation. He knows that there is an interaction of organisms with their environment and that if populations are separated by a physical barrier, the exertion of selection pressures can result in natural selection. He also appreciates that variation may be the result of mutations and that these are chance events. He knows that evolutionary changes take place over a long period of time.

Jack achieves 6 out of 6 marks.

Bethan's answer

(a) They are unable to breed to produce fertile offspring. ✗✓ ①

(b) Because the fish are in different lakes they can't breed together. ✗ ② They live in different places so their habitats are different ✓ ③ so over time they will have to adapt to their environments. This may lead to a change in their appearance. ✗ ③

Examiner commentary

① Bethan does not state that they interbreed or reproduce with each other but gains one mark for reference to 'fertile offspring'. ② She has poor expression and does not refer to 'populations' in her answer. ③ She gains a mark for mentioning that the habitats differ. However, she does not gain any more marks as she fails to use terms expected at this level. There is no mention of selection pressure, gene pools.

Bethan achieves 2 out of 6 marks.

Q&A 14

Genetic engineering involves the introduction of DNA from one species into another. Describe the process by which modified bacteria synthesise human insulin. *[10 marks]*

Mark scheme

① *Cells taken from pancreas* ② *Gene for insulin located* ③ *using gene/DNA probe* ④ *Use of restriction endonuclease enzyme* ⑤ *mRNA for insulin* ⑥ *Reverse transcriptase to make cDNA* ⑦ *DNA polymerase to convert cDNA to double strand* ⑧ *Sticky ends on gene* ⑨ *Use of bacterium as a vector as a source of* ⑩ *plasmids* ⑪ *Use of same restriction endonuclease* ⑫ *Sticky ends with complementary bases* ⑬ *Use of DNA ligase* ⑭ *Reference to marker genes for antibiotic resistance* ⑮ *Recombinant DNA* ⑯ *Reintroduced into bacterium.*

Jack's answer

There are two ways to make the human insulin gene. The first way is to find the mRNA strand that codes for the gene that codes for insulin ✓ ⑤ and using reverse transcriptase a cDNA strand can be made. ✓ ⑥ Free DNA nucleotides can then be attached and joined by hydrogen bonds between the complementary base pairs. DNA polymerase is used to anneal the sugar phosphate backbones. ✓ ⑦ The second method is to locate the exact gene that codes for insulin production ✓ ② and cut it out by the use of restriction endonuclease ✓ ⑤ which makes a staggered cut producing sticky ends. ✓ ⑧ A plasmid ✓ ⑩ is extracted from bacteria and is cut using the same restriction endonuclease ✓ ⑪ so that the base sequences from the DNA can base pair with those in the cut vector. ✓ ⑫ The foreign DNA is input into the vector and is held in place by hydrogen bonds between the complementary base pairs. DNA ligase ✓ ⑬ is then used to hold the foreign DNA in place in the vector. The plasmid is also joined with a marker gene so that when they add the plasmids to the bacteria they can determine which bacteria have taken up the plasmids successfully. A marker gene is usually antibiotic resistant ✓ ⑭ so that when antibiotics are added the bacteria that have incorporated the plasmid can be used to make human insulin.

Examiner commentary

③ ⑯ Mention of a gene probe and recombinant DNA are Jack's only omissions.

Summative comment

Jack's answer is very detailed and clearly written in a concise manner.
Jack achieves 10 out of 10 marks

Bethan's answer

To produce human insulin requires genetic engineering. A plasmid is cut out of a bacterium and the gene for insulin production is cut out from a human cell using restriction endonuclease. ✓ ④ Another enzyme allows for the sticky ends of the plasmid ✓ ⑨ to pair up with the complementary base pairs in the human gene. ✓ ⑫ The plasmid is then put back into the bacteria ✓ ⑯ and it can multiply producing human insulin. This is a high yielding and inexpensive method of producing human insulin.

Examiner commentary

Bethan refers to only one method of locating the template for insulin production. She has forgotten the name of the enzyme (DNA ligase) that anneals the 'sticky ends'. She also fails to include markers.

Summative comment

Bethan's answer suggests that she has a basic understanding of the process but her response is far too short and lacks detail.
Bethan achieves 4 out of 10 marks.

Q&A 15

Explain what is meant by the flow of energy through an ecosystem. Describe how energy is lost at each stage and comment on the efficiency of the transfer. Suggest reasons for any differences in efficiency. *[10 marks]*

Mark scheme

① *Energy is in the form of organic molecules passing from one trophic level to another* ② *Photosynthesis/light energy is converted to chemical energy* ③ *Photosynthesis is inefficient as not all wavelengths of light are absorbed* ④ *Energy not absorbed due to transmission and reflection* ⑤ *Loss of energy from plant by respiration* ⑥ *Reference to NPP and GPP* ⑦ *Efficiency of photosynthesis approx. 1%* ⑧ *Some parts of plant not eaten by herbivores* ⑨ *Loss by consumers due to respiration* ⑩ *Loss by consumers due to excretion* ⑪ *20% loss due to respiration and 60% due to excretion* ⑫ *Most energy taken up by decomposers* ⑬ *Secondary and tertiary consumers more efficient than primary consumers* ⑭ *Carnivores have a higher secondary productivity than herbivores* ⑮ *Reference to 10% energy passing from one trophic level to the next/ reference to protein rich diets and lack of cellulose in diet.*

Jack's answer

All energy is created by the sun. Solar energy enters the Earth's atmosphere as electromagnetic waves but most of these are absorbed or reflected. Photosynthetic organisms are the only organisms that can use the energy directly from sunlight to convert it into chemical energy. ✓ ② When lights falls onto a plant, only about 1% of the solar energy actually enters the plant. ✓ ⑦ Some light is at the wrong wavelength ✓ ③ for the photosystems and some light is reflected or transmitted by or through the plant. ✓ ④ Out of the energy that enters the plant 20% is used up in processes such as respiration ✓ ⑤ and photosynthesis. Photosynthesis results in the formation of energy in the form of glucose and this is why plants are known as producers. Energy is passed on to primary consumers (which can be herbivores which eat only plants or carnivores which eat only animals). They use this energy for metabolic processes and growth so energy is passed on from one trophic level to the next in a food chain. ✓ ① Energy is lost at each trophic level as heat energy as it is used for the metabolic processes. 10% of the total energy is passed from one trophic level to the next. ✓ ⑮ This is known as energy efficiency. Primary productivity is the energy created by plants. Secondary productivity is the energy available to the next trophic level compared to its total energy. ✗✗ ⑬ ⑭ The amount of energy used by a plant over the total solar energy that falls on its surface is known as photosynthetic efficiency. Food chains are limited to about four or five trophic levels due to the energy loss at each level and so there is insufficient energy to be passed on. The energy losses are due to respiration and excretion, ✓✓ ⑨ ⑩ approximately 20% is lost due to respiration and 60% loss in herbivores ✓ ⑪ as a lot of the plants they eat consist of cellulose. The loss due to excretion in secondary consumers is about 20% as they eat mainly protein which is easily digested.

When these organisms die and decay the energy is not wasted. In fact more energy passes into decomposers than into all the animals put together. ✓ ⑫ Decomposers such as bacteria and fungi obtain energy from decaying matter.

Examiner commentary

Jack has not used the terms 'net primary productivity and gross primary productivity'. ⑬ ⑭ He is unsure about the terms 'primary and secondary productivity'. He makes a vague statement that 'energy is created by plants' despite having made a correct statement ② about this earlier. Primary productivity is the food available to primary consumers. Secondary productivity is the rate at which consumers accumulate energy in the form of cells or tissues.

Summative comment

Jack has presented the essay in a logical and organised manner. He states clearly that light energy from the sun passes into plants for conversion to chemical energy. He explains why not all this energy is available to the plant. He uses biological terms appropriately and has a good overall understanding of the topic and how energy passes through the ecosystem.
Jack achieves 10 out of 10 marks.

Bethan's answer

Energy flow is the amount of energy passed on through each stage in a food chain in an ecosystem. ✗ ① The sun provides energy to the primary consumer although a lot of this energy is reflected and lost as heat back into the Earth's atmosphere. Also light may pass straight through the leaf instead of being absorbed. ✓ ④ The primary consumer only takes in about 10% of the energy when it eats plants. ✓ ⑮ Also the herbivore does not eat all of the plants available to it as it cannot get to the roots so some energy is left behind. ✓ ⑧ Energy is also lost due to respiration and excretion. ✓✓ ⑨ ⑩ About 60% of the energy lost in a herbivore is due to excretion. This is because plants contain cellulose and not all animals contain the enzyme to break it down. This means that the herbivore has to consume a lot of plants to provide itself with enough energy to survive. This means that the energy transfer between producer and primary consumer is not very efficient compared with the energy transfer between the primary consumer and the secondary consumer. ✓ ⑬ Although energy is still lost through respiration, and excretion the loss due to excretion is only about 20% compared to the herbivore's 60%. ✓ ⑪ This is because protein is more easily digested than plant material. The food chain usually stops at around four to five trophic levels as there would not be sufficient energy remaining to support another level.

Examiner commentary

① Bethan uses the term 'stage' instead of the correct term 'trophic level'.

Summative comment

Bethan's answer is promising but she has failed to achieve full marks as she does not mention some important points. She does not state that photosynthesis is inefficient and that not all wavelengths of energy are absorbed. There is no reference to net primary productivity and gross primary productivity. Also she fails to refer to herbivores having a lower secondary productivity than carnivores.

Bethan achieves 7 out of 10 marks.

Q & A

16

The table shows the estimates of the percentage of various habitats that have been lost in the UK since 1900.

Habitat	Loss since 1900	Reason for habitat loss
Hay meadow	95	Conversion to grass and silage
Chalk grassland	80	Conversion to grass and silage
Lowland fens and wetlands	50	Reclamation for agriculture
Limestone	45	Removal for sale for garden rockeries
Lowland heath	40	Conversion to grassland and commercial forest
Lowland mixed woodland	40	Conversion to commercial conifer plantations and farmland
Hedgerows	30	Fields enlarged to accommodate farm machinery

(a) Suggest one benefit and one risk associated with the conversion of hay meadows and chalk grassland to highly productive grass and silage. [2]

(b) Some lowland mixed woodlands have been replaced by monocultures such as woodland. How this change might result in lower species diversity. [1]

(c) How might the information in the table provide evidence to a committee on preserving habitats and biodiversity? [3]

(d) The European Union gives grants to farmers to replant hedges. Explain how replanting hedges affects species diversity. [1]

[total = 7 marks]

Jack's answer

(a) Benefit: cheaper grazing and fodder costs. ✓
Risk: loss of species diversity. ✓ ①

(b) A monoculture is where one species is grown, whereas mixed woodlands consist of many species. ✓

(c) The table shows where most change has taken place and therefore the habitats at most risk. These could be placed in an order of priority and measures decided to conserve them. ✓✗✗ ②

(d) Hedges provide more habitats for species. Therefore species diversity is increased. ✓

Examiner commentary

① Another possible answer would be 'fewer fertilisers and pesticides needed'. ② Jack should observe from the mark allocation that he needs to make three points. He should have built on the information provided in the table adding to his answer examples of measures of conservation such as providing grants for farmers to re-establish hay meadows, natural woodlands and hedgerows. Legislation could be introduced to prevent habitat destruction, the construction of drainage ditches and rock removal.

Jack achieves 5 out of 7 marks.

Bethan's answer

(a) Benefit: less use of pesticides and fertilisers. ✓
Risk: more pesticides and fertilisers needed. ✗ ①

(b) Mixed woodlands are made up of many different species of trees but something like a pine forest is a single species. ✓

(c) They could be told what changes have taken place over the last 100 years so that the committee can decide what to do. ✗✗✗ ②

(d) Hedges are places where plants and animals live so the more hedges the more plants and animals there will be. ✓

Examiner commentary

① Bethan is 'hedging her bets' and achieves one mark.
② Bethan has not used the information in the table and consequently provides no information for the committee to consider.

Bethan achieves 3 out of 7 marks.

Quickfire answers:

BY4 Metabolism, Microbiology and Homeostasis

① Muscle, liver.

② The energy is released rapidly, in a single step and is transferred directly to the reaction requiring it.

③ (a) Cytoplasm.
(b) Matrix of mitochondrion.

④ Oxygen is the final electron acceptor. Without it electrons would accumulate along the chain and the reaction would come to a halt.

⑤ Provides a large surface area for the attachment of the electron carriers that transfer electrons along the chain.

⑥ $\frac{2 \times 30 \times 100}{2880} = 2\%$

⑦ Fat.

⑧ ATP and reduced NADP.

⑨ The bacteria moved to where oxygen was produced the most, at the blue and red wavelengths.

⑩ Action spectrum shows the rate of photosynthesis at different wavelengths of light, whereas absorption spectrum indicates how much light a particular pigment absorbs at each wavelength.

⑪ A single pigment absorbs only a limited part of the spectrum. Additional pigments increase the range of wavelengths absorbed.

⑫ Chlorophyll a.

⑬ Water – photolysis.

⑭ Oxygen.

⑮ Cyclic involves only PSI, source of electrons PSI, final electron acceptor PSI.
Non-cyclic involves PSI and PSII, source of electrons water, PSII, final electron acceptor reduced NADP.

⑯ So that it can accept additional carbon dioxide, otherwise the cycle could not continue.

⑰ Round and spherical.

⑱ Lipopolysaccharide.

⑲ Red/pink.

⑳ Suitable temperature, suitable pH, carbon source/glucose, nitrogen source.

㉑ At 37°C pathogens are more likely to reproduce.

㉒ Gram-positive bacteria such as *Clostridium* produce resistant endospores which are resistant to temperatures of 100°C.

㉓ Each colony develops from a single bacterium.

㉔ Asexual reproduction.

㉕ Rapid rate of growth, more efficient due to high yield, carried out at lower temperatures.

㉖ Ammonia contains nitrogen which is needed to synthesise proteins.

㉗ To prevent over-heating from the heat generated by microbial metabolism. The increased temperature would otherwise denature the enzymes.

㉘ This reflects the need of the free-living organism to reduce competition.

㉙ This is a period of preparation for growth and enzymes are produced by protein synthesis.

㉚ The maximum population size that can be supported by the available resources.

㉛ Density dependent – the effect depends on the population size.
Density independent – effect is the same no matter what the population size.

㉜ Lack of food, predation, parasitism, toxic waste.

㉝ Interspecific.

㉞ Specific, non-persistent and should not accumulate and be passed along food chains.

㉟ Species highly specific, long-term, no environmental contamination.

㊱ Chemicals are non-specific and would kill the wasp, long term residual effect, waste of money.

㊲ Carbon dioxide levels increase due to increased combustion of fossil fuels; deforestation so less photosynthesis.

㊳ Nitrate is combined with the products of photosynthesis to form amino acids which are converted to proteins required for growth.

㊴ Nitrification.

㊵ Denitrification, leaching, crop removal/ harvesting, deforestation.

㊶ If the information is not fed back once an effector has corrected any deviation and returned the system to the set point, the receptor will continue to stimulate the effector and an over correction will lead to a deviation in the opposite direction to the original.

㊷ (a) (i) Osmoreceptors in hypothalamus.
(ii) Kidney.
(b) Hormones are transported in the blood plasma.

㊸ Cortex.

㊹ Increase the pressure in the glomerulus.

㊺ Proximal convoluted tubule.

㊻ Microvilli; numerous mitochondria.

㊼ (a) Osmoreceptors of hypothalamus.
(b) Pituitary gland.

㊽ Uric acid.

㊾ A – kangaroo rat B – cat
C – beaver.

㊿ They are rapid as the neurone pathway is short with usually one or two synapses. They are protective in function.

(51) Under the microscope the grey area is seen to contain the cell bodies of neurones.

(52) As the extensions are short and branch in a number of different directions, the transmission is slow.

(53) Motor.

(54) −70mV.

(55) Another action potential cannot be generated until the resting potential is restored. This ensures a unidirectional impulse and prevents impulses from merging.

(56) Myelination; diameter of the axon.

(57) The mitochondria provide ATP needed to resynthesise the neurotransmitter.

(58) Facilitated diffusion.

(59) Acetylcholine is broken down by cholinesterase and the components reform on the other side of the synaptic cleft.

(60) Florigen in the leaves.

(61) A – Dark period is short enough for long-day plants to flower but not long enough for short-day ones to do so.
B – As there is no single long light period and yet long-day plants flower it must be the short dark period that is the critical factor inducing flowering.
C – The dark period is long enough for short-day plants to flower but not short enough for the long-day ones to do so.
D – The short light period in the middle of the dark period prevents short-day plants flowering as there is no single long dark period. Each dark period is, however, short enough to induce flowering in long-day plants.

(62) Allows plant breeders to cross-pollinate flowers which would not normally flower at the same time; preparation of flowering plants for known dates such as Christmas, Easter.

BY5 Environment, Genetics and Evolution

① While the nucleotides would match up to their complementary nucleotides on the original DNA strand, they would not join together to form a new strand.

② To prevent contamination, so ^{15}N is not incorporated into a new strand.

③ As half the original DNA is built into the new DNA strand.

④ CGTAATCG.

⑤ 24.

⑥ A different base may code for a different amino acid and so the sequence of amino acids in the polypeptide produced will be different.

⑦ GGU/CCU/CUC/UUA/AGU/AAA
Six.

⑧ TAG on DNA
UAG on tRNA.

⑨ (a) mRNA (b) tRNA (c) DNA.

⑩ Homologous chromosomes do not pair up during prophase of mitosis but pair up to form bivalents in prophase 1 of meiosis.

⑪ One of the two copies of a chromosome that are joined together by a single centromere prior to cell division.

⑫ Recombination by crossing over. Independent assortment.

⑬ Mitosis – 2. Meiosis – 4.

⑭ (a) 63.
(b) Gametes are produced by meiosis, homologous chromosomes need to pair. This is not possible with 63 chromosomes, therefore meiosis cannot take place and so gametes cannot be produced.

⑮ Haploid refers to sex cells or gametes that contain only a single copy of each chromosome. Diploid applies to cells in which the nucleus contains two sets of chromosomes.

⑯ Seminiferous tubules.

⑰ Seminal vesicle and prostate gland.

⑱ To provide ATP for movement.

⑲ (a) To nourish the spermatids and protect them from the immune system.
(b) Secrete testosterone, the male hormone.

⑳ The fusion of the sperm with the ovum.

㉑ Zygote.

㉒ So that the organism becomes independent of water as the sperm is introduced directly into the female tract.

㉓ To soften the layer of cells surrounding the oocyte to enable the sperm to penetrate the egg.

㉔ To prevent the entry of further sperm.

㉕ Urine of a pregnant female contains the hormone hCG.

㉖ hCG.

㉗ The antibody hCG forms a blue bead complex with the first antibody. This complex binds to the antibody in the large window and prevents it diffusing any further.

㉘ Ovary, style, stigma.

㉙ Self-pollination is the transfer of pollen to the stigma of the same flower, whereas cross-pollination is the transfer to another flower on another plant of the same species.

㉚ Due to chance much of the pollen fails to reach the stigma of another flower and so is wasted.

㉛ A tough wall to prevent drying out; sculptured, spiky surface to attach to insects.

㉜ To control the growth of the pollen tube.

㉝ The secretion of enzyme to digest a path and also may provide nutrients for growth.

㉞ One of the male nuclei from the pollen tube fuses with both polar nuclei in the embryo sac.

㉟ Pollination is the transfer of pollen to the stigma, whereas fertilisation is the fusion of male and female gametes.

㊱ So the energy is made available via respiration for metabolism and growth.

㊲ For anchorage and water uptake.

㊳ Plumule, radicle.

㊴ Food reserves run out before the leaves open above ground and it will not be able to photosynthesise to make more food.

㊵ Expresses itself only in the presence of another identical allele. The effect of the allele is apparent in the phenotype of the diploid organism only.

㊶ 1/16 x 96/1 = 6.

㊷ A gene that is carried on either the X or Y chromosome.

㊸ 5–10%.

㊹ Most mutations are recessive and the recessive allele is not expressed in the genotype.

㊺ Bacteria have a short life cycle and show a greater rate of mutation.

㊻ Xrays, gamma radiation, UV light, certain mutagenic chemicals.

㊼ Carcinogen.

㊽ Gene and chromosome.

㊾ 1 in 4 – 25%.

㊿ (a) Breakdown of spindle fibres during cell division/non-disjunction; chromatids don't separate.
(b) Pairing of homologous chromosomes cannot take place; no meiosis and no gametes produced.

(51) Tar.

(52) Discontinuous.

(53) Mutation.

(54) Crossing over, independent assortment, alleles contributed from each parent.

(55) The environmental force altering the frequency of alleles in a population.

(56) Predation/competition/carrying capacity is reached.

(57) When a physical barrier, such as a mountain, prevents two populations from interbreeding.

(58) Surrogate.

(59) No variation.

(60) Production of a single identical genetic line of cells with desirable characteristics to maintain genetic stocks.

(61) Skin graft, organs for transplantation.

(62) To prevent fungal growth.

(63) Differentiation.

(64) Uniform crop, storage and transport.

(65) Sterile conditions, genetically unstable.

(66) Get into nucleus; join the DNA of the cells; protein synthesis; reinserted into membrane.

(67) A recombinant gene may pass from the organism it was placed in, to a completely different organism. Perhaps a virus might transfer genes for herbicide resistance from a crop plant to a weed. Genetically modified bacteria often have antibiotic resistance marker genes added. This antibiotic resistance could be transferred to harmful bacteria.

(68) Contains only the gene required/not unwanted gene; doesn't carry junk DNA/introns. Process doesn't produce a variety of other fragments which need to be screened out.

(69) To show which bacterial cells have taken up the plasmid.

(70) Pollen may be transferred to other plants introducing features such as herbicide resistance which would be detrimental if transferred to weed species.

(71) Restriction endonuclease.

(72) Hydrogen.

(73) Biological contaminants may contain DNA and this DNA would be copied.

(74) To increase the quantity of DNA because the sample obtained from a crime scene may be very small.

(75) Replacing defective gene with a healthy gene in the fertilised egg.

(76) A protein rich diet is more readily and efficiently digested; no energy-consuming symbionts in the digestive tract; faeces contain less undigested matter as there is no cellulose in the diet.

(77) Primary succession involves the introduction of plants and animals into an area that has not previously supported a community.
Secondary succession refers to the reintroduction of organisms into an area previously occupied but perhaps destroyed by fire.

(78) Trees, e.g. oak.

(79) They produce the enzyme, penicillinase which makes penicillin ineffective.

(80) Increases the chance of two harmful recessive genes combining.

(81) Loss of habitat, over-hunting by humans, competition from introduced species.

(82) Mineral depletion, increase in pests and diseases.

(83) Climate change, soil erosion, destruction of natural habitats.

(84) Lack of roots binding soil together resulting in rainfall washing the soil away.

(85) Oil seed rape.

(86) Brazil.

(87) Pre-treatment of cellulose prior to fermentation.

(88) Quotas, restricting net mesh size, limits to catches, restricted times of year for fishing.

(89) Antibiotics, pesticides.

(90) Burning of fossil fuels; deforestation.

(91) Restrict the quantity of fertiliser added to soil, only apply fertiliser when crops are growing, leave a 10-metre strip between land and waterway.